OUTTA MY SYSTEM

KATEE THOMPSON HUYGHUE

Front Cover Image by Beyond The Book Media
Book Design by Beyond The Book Media
First printing edition 2020

Contents

Acknowledgments

First, I want to thank ME. I want to thank me for trusting God and believing his promises. I thank me for NEVER giving up. I want to thank God for always knowing that I would be a writer and for revealing that to me from the time I was 3 years old.

Next, I want to thank my publisher Chanel Martin, for starting a Facebook 7 Day Writing Challenge called Write With Me. I stumbled upon it and thought "there's no way I can finish this idea for a novel in 7 days", but I did. I want to thank Chanel for her belief, push, drive and support, but mainly for allowing me to write such a raw, secular novel within this primarily Christian based group. Thank you for allowing me to spit out My story. Thank you to my Grandfather, Limmie Thompson (RIP), for telling me since I was 4 years old that I could and would achieve every dream I had.

I also have to thank several family members who encouraged a little 4 Eyed girl who always had a book in her hand, even when everyone else's comment was "why do you always have a book?!!" Thank you, Mom, Aunt V'Niques, Aunt Honey (RIP) and last but definitely not least, Aunt Janet for knowing I was a Butterfly before I did.

Preface

I had an epiphany last night....

I've always heard that if you repeat a behavior for twenty-one days, it becomes a habit that you will adopt, like working out at the gym. OR, if you STOP doing something for twenty-one days, such as smoking cigarettes, it's easier to not return to that habit. Now, I don't know if that's really true, but I figured...if life really does work that way, shouldn't it also work on falling out of love???

After all, isn't a bad love relationship just another bad habit?

My ex-boyfriend is stuck under my skin, and I HAVE to do whatever I can to dig him out. Over the last six years, we have officially broken up (yes, I said six YEARS), and tried to get back together at least three times a year, without success. Yeah, there were good reasons each attempt hadn't worked, but in my opinion, anything can be worked out if two people genuinely love each other and want to be together. After that last time, I finally figured out he really didn't want to be with me and didn't really love me, at least not the way I wanted to be loved. He just wanted me when he wanted me in the way that he wanted me. I don't even know if he was capable of the kind of love I wanted. Perhaps in his own screwed up way – he did love me. It just wasn't the kind of love I wanted Or THOUGHT that I deserved.

In all honesty, as embarrassing as it is to admit, if this man had said to me, "Baby, I love you and want to try to build a life with you. Come back to Arizona and be with me," I would have run my happy little ass right on back to Phoenix.

OH!! Did I forget to mention the Phoenix, Arizona part?

Okay, what I should do is give you a little rundown on the history of the relationship so you can understand what was REALLY going on. Then, I'll take you with me on my twenty-one-day journey….

2001: The Best Day...Or The Worst Day

I HAD INITIALLY MOVED to Arizona several years before, just for a change of pace. Like a lot of Arizona transplants from California, I had gotten tired of the "fast-paced, fake friends, everybody on a diet, too expensive to live, and if we keep it all the way real, so much to do that you actually do a lot of nothing." After a bad and even uglier divorce, my children and I needed a change. My ex-husband wasn't in the picture, so I decided to get out of California. My two adult children decided to stay in Arizona since they had families, jobs, relationships, close friends, and, well....LIVES. I was going to miss them, but it was only a four and a half-hour drive or a fifty-minute flight, so I decided we would all be okay.

I didn't date for a while because priorities were finding a great job, getting my credit right, save some money, and stabilizing my two younger children after the BIG move. After about six months, I was open to dating, but I wasn't looking with intention.

When I first met HIM (His name will be HIM because he doesn't deserve any more attention than that), he was the kind of man a woman dreams about dating. He wooed me relentlessly, especially considering that I was already dating a friend of his. (Should have known something was wrong with his ass then – what kind of man intentionally goes after his friend's girl???) DON'T JUDGE ME, he wasn't MY friend!!! Oh, he was good. He casually "let it slip" that old boy was married – how'd I miss that? Anyways, I was a loan officer, and he was a Real Estate Investor. His friend gave him my phone number because he thought we could do some work together. I knew from the beginning he was attracted to me. He would show up at my office randomly, and I have to admit, I was impressed. Not attracted, mind you, because I didn't think he was especially attractive, but impressed because he was relentless and sweet. He would show up, ask me to go to lunch with him to "discuss business" and sometimes just drop off a Caribbean beer for my friend, Mike and I. My boss was getting a little annoyed because he thought I was wasting my time, and that we weren't going to be able to do business with him. At the time, I thought he was just jealous. Later, I found out that was not the case because he was having sex with his foster son. WELL...But that's a whole other story.

Anyway, back to HIM. He must have asked me out about ten times, and each time I would remind him that I was dating his friend. He would say, "we're not friends, we're just acquaintances." SCANDALOUS!!!!!

So, one day, I find out that my cousin, Tina, and her husband are coming to town. The day they arrive just happens to be the day that HIM's loan was closing escrow. So, I take Tina to the office with me, and she meets HIM. He is, of course, in his element and being what he can be... charming as hell. HIM, asks Tina if he can take her and her husband to dinner (because he figured I couldn't say no). Of course, she says yes. We go to Macaroni Grill and have a FANTASTIC time.

After dinner, he realizes that he's "locked his keys in the car"...hmmm. So, I have to take my cousin to my house, come back, and take HIM to his house to get his spare keys. We get there, one thing leads to another, and well...The next day, I realize we're in a relationship.

It was good. It was the kind of love affair Alicia Keys writes songs about. Passion, fire, and desire. We couldn't stand to be away from each other for more than a few hours. If he was working, I took him lunch. When I went out of town, he called me every day, and the day I got back in town, it was like we had been apart for months, even though it was only days. Our friends and his relatives were jealous. They always told us, "You two make me sick – no one can be that much in love." You know, that "Notebook," "never leaving your ass" kind of love. He was six feet three inches tall, over 200 pounds with muscles that made me breathe hard when I felt them. I could have an orgasm just squeezing his arms sometimes.

But, his insecurity and jealousy began to filter through. In reality, I began to think HIM just didn't LIKE women...I don't know what happened to him in his past relationships with women or girls, but it couldn't have been good. I mean, he LOVES women, but he doesn't particularly think a lot of them. And, because I'm a friendly person, especially towards men, some might call me flirtatious. I just say that I know how to be sweet. The combination wasn't right. We're both independent, fiery, and obstinate people. One of us needed to give in, but neither of us could. So, we kept going...break up... makeup. Until it got ugly. Until HIM got ugly. His insecurity took over to the point that he became cruel towards me. I figured it was a protection for himself because of his past, protection against what he thought I would do to him. HIM would invite me to an outing with his friends or family, and then totally ignore me. But, when we were alone, he was insatiable sexually. He couldn't get enough of my body. It was almost as if he wanted me so badly, but hated that he wanted me that bad.

There were lots of other instances of his cruelty, and I spent many nights crying. But, that's not this story…That's a WHOLE different story. But, I will tell you about the straw that broke this camel's back…

2005: The Straw...The Camel....The Broke Back...

I WAS DIAGNOSED with breast cancer and was six months into my cancer treatment. He was "kinda" there for me, but not really. During that time, I had maintained a deep friendship with a guy I worked with, Mike, and an "on the surface" friendship with a woman I met through Mike. Her name was Michelle. Well, Mike died during a nasty and "questionable" incident with the police while I was at a training session for Mortgage Brokers. While I was at that session, one of my lender representatives called me and told me that Mike had been killed. I was devastated. I called Michelle, and she confirmed his death. She was upset because they had worked together and become close. I kept trying to call HIM because I was so upset. I'd known Mike for about three years. Hell, I'd gotten my first DUI hanging out with Mike. But I couldn't reach HIM.

I found out the next day that the reason HIM wasn't returning my call was because he was with Michelle consoling her! When I found out, I was beyond hurt. While I was alone mourning the loss of a friend I'd had for three years, HIM was at her house consoling her? Well, that pretty much let me know that HIM was in a relationship with her. It doesn't take a Rocket Scientist to add one plus one. That shit ALWAYS adds up to two!! And, this was supposed to be my friend? She had actually even taken me to one of my chemo treatments. And, all the while, they were in a relationship. I felt so betrayed. That's when I decided to get out of Phoenix. I had to, I was slowly dying inside...and not from cancer.

I went back to California in May of 2005. From that time until May of 2010, we got back together at least five times a year – with either me going to Phoenix to see him or him coming to California to see me. Each time, it ended ugly – with him treating me bad and me shutting him out. We were like a drug for each other. We couldn't stay away from each other, but we really didn't like what each other was...IT WAS CRAZY.

In May of 2010 – we decided to meet in Las Vegas. I was taking my sister for her birthday, and he wanted an excuse to see me. He talked about us working something out, I thought, o.k., we'll see what happens. As usual, it was thunder and lightning. From the moment we saw each other, we wanted each other. The sexual tension was deafening. As soon as I could escape my sister, I went to his room. For the next two nights, we made incredible love each night.

It was inevitable...I don't even remember what it was, but he pissed me off. I walked away, and he let me. I don't even know how I got back to my room because I had been drinking all day and night; was tore up from the floor up. The next day, we were cold towards each other, but at the end of the night, I knew we needed to talk. So, I tried to call him all night. NO ANSWER...

I left him a message saying that not only were we not lovers, but we weren't even friends anymore, and to please never call me again. It was time he let me go. You know, just all in my feelings and pissed off.

Once again, I was through. Or, so I thought.

We didn't speak for a couple of weeks, and then I went to

Phoenix AGAIN for a two-week trip at the end of September 2010. I was going for my granddaughter's birthday, and it was a well-needed vacation. I will admit that by then, a part of me was hoping to spend some time with HIM. But I knew I shouldn't. I guess I was there for three days before I broke down and went to his house. Of course, we had sex that night. The next morning, I felt like such a fool. What was I doing? I left while he was at work. He called me, but I didn't answer the phone. He called me again, and this time, I answered. He was sweet and told me that he was going out of town that day and would be back the next day and wanted to call me. I told him o.k.; I'd talk to him then.

Now, I have that stupid hope again. But, that next day, I didn't hear from him. So, two days later, I'm upset, and I call him. No answer. I called him the next day and left him a message just saying that I made a big mistake, and I didn't understand why he wasn't man enough to tell me that I was just a booty call that night. At least be honest!!! Once again, I was devastated. Two days passed, and he called me. By then, I didn't want to talk to him, so I didn't answer the phone.

I decided then that I had to kick this addiction, or it would kill me, or I would kill HIM.

So, THAT was the beginning of my 21-Days to break this really bad, fucked up, habit!

Day 1: The Brutal Truth

Monday, September 6, 2010

I WOKE up at about 8:30 a.m., but since I was on vacation and there was no reason for me to be awake so early, I decided to sleep in knowing that would eat up some of the hours of the day. As soon as I woke up, I checked my cell phone to see if I had a missed call from HIM. I was kind of relieved that I had forgotten to charge my phone last night, so it was dead. THANK GOD for my sorry ass Blackberry. My charger was in the car, and it was way too much work for me to go outside just to get a little juice and STILL be disappointed. So, I rolled over and slept four more hours...

Well, it's 12:30 in the afternoon now. I guess I can face DAY 1 of "KICKING THE LOVE HABIT." You see, distraction is really important when you're trying to kick a bad habit. I washed my face, brushed my teeth, and went looking for my grandson. My granddaughter was at school, but maybe my favorite grandson can show me how to bowl on his Wii game.

NOOOOOO!!!!!

I'm walking all through the apartment, and no Grandson!!! Where was everybody??!!

What am I gonna do now?

I HONESTLY DON'T UNDERSTAND HOW HE CAN SAY HE'S STILL IN LOVE WITH ME, KNOW I'M IN TOWN, SPEND THE NIGHT WITH ME, AND NOT CALL ME OR RETURN MY CALL!!!!

Stop, Stop, Stop!!!!! There I go again, back to obsessing on HIM. A distraction is seriously needed…NOW!!!

Let me remind you: I arrived in Arizona Saturday, texted him Monday – no response. Showed up on his doorstep Friday at 5:30 a.m., had sex with him & left. He called me at noon – small chitchat. It's Saturday, again, I texted and called him – no response. NOW, IT'S MONDAY! A whole other week later.

SMDH….

I know what I'll do, I'll make a list of why I want to be with him and another list about why I shouldn't be with him. Maybe if I see the shit on paper, my dumb ass can move on.

WHY I DO:

1. He'll always take care of me
2. He's 6'3" – I love tall men
3. He's strong
4. He's handy around the house
5. The sex is AWESOME

WHY I DON'T:

1. He's rude
2. He's very arrogant
3. He doesn't show feelings
4. He shuts down emotionally without any reason

5. He's an asshole
6. He doesn't agree with my standard of living
7. He doesn't adore me
8. He doesn't seem to "like" women
9. He doesn't trust women
10. He just wants a woman to "produce his heir."
11. His focus is primarily money
12. He doesn't like Christians

Wait! O.K., I don't think I need any more WHY I DON'T's. I know some of my don'ts may sound cruel, but I'm just brutally honest. Also, he's always saying that people who talk about GOD can't be trusted, and the minute someone says they're a Christian, he shuts them off.

DAMN HEATHEN!!! That should have been enough to scare me straight!!

I'm a Christian (YES, I AM!), and I want a Christian man who adores me, but also someone who has the means and, more importantly, the desire to take care of me. And, I want someone nice, someone that all of my friends would be jealous that I have, even though I know that's petty as hell. I don't want an asshole, which he is.

Okay, I think it worked…For now, anyway, he sounds REAL unattractive. So, I decided to watch some T.V.

Aaaah…yeah…Law & Order reruns always does the trick. I'm just trying to avoid a Xanax.

It's about three p.m., so I think it's time for some lunch and a drink. Oh, don't get your panties in a bunch!!! I'm on vacation, so I'm allowed to drink all day if I want to!! I fix my drink, and I'm just lying on the sofa eating a sandwich and drinking a vodka and orange juice mix when I figure it out. I know that the best distraction is gonna be another man thinking that I'm attractive, so I decide to get dressed and go trolling. I got dressed, but I wanted REAL attention, so I dressed sexy casual. Denim stretch jeans from Nordstrom's that hug my small butt right and make my waist look tiny, a yellow tank top, and some bronze flip flops would do the trick. I put my hair up in a high ponytail with long bangs sweeping to the side. No make-up (too damn dry and hot for all that - I'd be sweating and huffing like a pig), but a touch of Chanel lip gloss...perfect!!! – HAD THAT BRAZILIAN WAVY HAIR SWANGING BEHIND ME...

I drove to Fry's Supermarket – I need some more juice for my vodka. I parked the car, and as I walked towards the store, like a model on the runway (in my mind), I heard a voice behind me say, "Don't break any hearts today." I smile as I turn around towards the angel GOD sent to tell me that. "Excuse me?" I purr because, of course, I heard it, but I want to hear it again. An older gentleman is grinning his head off – "I'm just saying that you must break plenty of hearts, so don't break any today." Oh, I'm in seventh heaven now. I smiled again and said, "Okaaaay, I'll do my best," flipped my Brazilian ponytail (I swear, there's something about a woman with a long ponytail that drives these men crazy), and walk into the store. I pick up some cranberry juice, you know for my vodka and some Gogurts for the grandkids. I'm picking out the Gogurts, and some 19-year-old guy steps up to me and says, "Hi, how are you?" I frown and say, "Hello, I'm good." He's still standing there grinning, so I say, "Can I help you?" He still has that nineteen-year-old silly grin on his face and says, "Are you from around here?" Cute.... then I realize that he's hitting on me....Cute... Hahaha, I still got it!! I pay for my juice and Gogurts and head to the liquor store to get my vodka. Haha, liquor store man hits on me too.

Jesus done fixed it !!

I'm driving back to the apartment, smiling and thinking, "That asshole didn't know what he had." I know you're thinking, "How vain!" But, I need this right now... bad. I've made it to the end of the day without calling HIM. I'm on my way to recovery.

I have made it through the whole day and almost through the evening when my phone starts ringing. I look down at the phone, and it's that asshole calling. I just watched the phone and kinda dance to my Sex and the City ringtone. Fuck him. I'm not answering. He didn't leave a message.... wonder what he wanted. But this is good. Now I'm pissed that he did call. Fuck you for calling me after three days. Fuck you and the horse you rode in on!!! I need to call the only person who will understand how I feel right now. That's my Girl, Marilyn, cause she's still in love with an asshole who doesn't want her either.

9:45 p.m. - I have to be honest, I'm sad. I miss him, I miss us. But, the "him" and the "us" that I miss is the 2002 him and us. I'm proud of myself. I didn't answer his call, and now I want to go home.

12:28 a.m. – I'm still thinking about that asshole. I actually visualized him knocking on the door, crying that he'd made a mistake, saying that he still loved me and would I please be with him again. But, I didn't call him, and his sorry ass never knocked on the door.

Day 2: What Else Would Be in Scottsdale?

I WOKE up early this morning feeling good. I wasn't craving the asshole at all. I'll admit it, I'm still all in my feelings, but I decided to start the day early. So, I hopped out of bed, excited for the day, and drove to my oldest daughter's house to pick up my youngest daughter for breakfast. I figured I may as well check my e-mail. I've given up thinking that I'm on vacation, I'm just out of town.

Yes, Lord!! I received the HUD approval from GMAC on my transaction. Now, we can fund and record. This was probably the worst real estate transaction of my career so far. NOT because it was hard, but because I wasn't supposed to have to deal with it while I was on vacation. But, it's O.K., I think I'll buy myself a lovely Louis Vuitton wallet to reward myself for getting it done. Gloria, my escrow officer, sent me an e-mail, "We couldn't have gotten it closed without you." I LOVE that woman!! That made me feel so good that I'm actually O.K. with working on my vacation.

Breakfast was good, a little spot in Downtown Phoenix called Matt's Big Breakfast. Great food and customer service and two people for $10??!! Come on! One thing I do love about Phoenix is that people have that Southwest hospitality and say 'Good Morning.' I Love it. Most Californians walk by you like you don't even exist.

We headed on over to Biltmore Fashion Park. It was starting to be such a good day, so I think I'll buy myself a couple of summer dresses, my oldest daughter some Coach sneakers, and my youngest daughter that Juicy Couture purse she wanted.

Oh, I love it here! These men stare with no shame! Men in Southern California act like they're too cool to let you know they're interested.

WAIT!! I just realized that the men that are showing me attention are all White men!! Could that be the problem??!! Maybe I'm on the wrong team! DAMN! Is that it - was the Ego of a Black Man too large to mix with my vanity and desire to be spoiled? Don't even let me get started down that road, because that's a 200 plus-year-old problem that Black Men and Women won't ever see eye to eye on. Besides, what else would be in Scottsdale, except White men? And, as my mother has always said, "We do Not discriminate in this family!"

Hmmmmmmm! I got some thinking to do.

6 p.m. – I'm going to a sports bar to watch the Laker game with my oldest daughter, her Manfriend and a couple of their friends.

Random thought...

Why do Laker fans call the NBA games "**THE LAKER GAME?** As if it's already pre-determined that the Lakers own the game?

I'm not a sports fan, as a matter of fact, the only teams I like are any that Michael Jordan played on, or will ever play on again (I don't care if he's sixty-five years old!) So, the Lakers are playing Boston, and I walk into the sports bar with a Phoenix Suns jersey on because that's just me, and what better way to have a bar full of men notice me? ESPE-CIALLY since I'm IN Phoenix, representing!

It's the evening of Day 2, it's been a minute, and I'm starting to re-live sex with HIM in my head, and I'm feening...this ain't good.

So, I strut my little butt (look, I ain't exactly got junk in the trunk, but I know how to work what I got) into Majerle's Sports Grill. It's a hopping sports bars in Phoenix with THE BEST hot wings and buffalo shrimp (In my humble opinion). I make my way to the back of the bar. Since the game had started about an hour before I got there, it's packed. I liked that because it means I got myself a full audience.

I had planned on only drinking water. Being drunk, trying to get over a man, a room full of men who probably have one thing on their mind, repeated flashbacks to sex, plus my high sex drive? That would not lead to anything nice. But, I do allow two gentlemen to sit with me, pay for my meal and buy me a Sprite as I pretended to know less about basketball then I really do. Which don't take a whole lot of pretending, trust me! The tall one (remember I like them tall) asks me how long I'll be in Phoenix. I get my Marilyn Monroe attitude on, tilt my head slightly, peering at him under my bangs, and say, "For two more days ... whyyy?" He looks me directly in my eyes (GOD, I love a bold man who will look me in my eyes, snatch me by my $750 weave, pull me to him .... Oh, sorry...I digress) and whisper (his lips one inch from mine) "Just wanted to know how much longer I have to get you to like me." Wowww, good thing I'm taking my recovery seriously. But, it's a distraction, right?

Third quarter, Lakers up by twelve points and we're outta here.

Two hours later......

I know what you're thinking!

No!

I did not have sexual relations with that man! He walked me outside, we exchanged numbers with the promise (probably empty) to keep in touch, and maybe he'll visit me in California.

I went home folks, and I feel wonderful because even though I thought about HIM today, I didn't want to be with him TODAY. I keep thinking about a conversation I had with one of my aunts, whom I always admired and adored. She went through drug addiction and just stopped one day. I asked her, "How did you just stop one day and to my knowledge never sunk low again. She looked at me and said, "whenever I get a craving, I fast forward to AFTER I allowed myself to do crack, and that picture is enough to make me say "NO" today." That always stuck with me. Well, that's how I need to treat my addiction when I have the desire to call HIM, answer his calls, go to his house, have sex with him, and give him ONE MORE CHANCE. I need to fast forward. Fast forward to the part where he ignores me again, doesn't call me for two weeks, isn't sure what he wants, doesn't know if he believes in LOVE. That same tired story that I'm over.

I can't do that again! I don't need him. He drains ALL my fabulosity, and we can't have that, can we??!

Day 3: Bust The Windows Out His Car

I WOKE UP, and I felt good. Even though I was a little sad that it was my last day in Phoenix, I was a bit anxious to get home. I just wanted to get away from HIM and get back to work and into my own bed.

"I did" trumps "I will" all day, every day. I'm so happy that "I did" resist HIM this entire time. But, deep down, I can't believe I was able to resist him because I do realize that I have this weakness that I can't explain or understand. I've had better looking, better acting, better at making money, and better at treating me. There is something about him that kept bringing me back. Together, we're explosive, but it wasn't always a good explosion!

I waited for my granddaughter to get out of school, and then we went to the game store to get another controller for her Wii game that her dad had bought her. He only bought one damn controller, and she and my grandson will kill each other, trying to share one.

As we drove back from the store, all of a sudden, I got the biggest urge to just drive to HIM's house. I mean, what would it hurt? It's not like anything would or could happen. I had my grandchild with me. I swear, I was trying to delay, but that drug was calling me! I don't know how drug addicts resist. I finally think I understand that pull. All I can think about are the good times right now. It's getting harder to fast forward to what always happens – me getting my heartbroken. Mmmm, we're driving by Chipotle. I think I'll stop and get a chicken burrito bowl. I'm hungry, so I can't think. Maybe after I eat, I can make a decision that I won't regret tomorrow.

I was finishing up my food and, God help me, but I still wanted to drive to his house. So, we headed over – me and what I hope is my deterrent to fall into his arms, my grand-daughter being with me. I was heading up Central Avenue and getting ready to turn onto Camelback Road, and I had a flashback to another instance of HIM doing me wrong. I remembered driving up Camelback Road to his house-warming party when he bought his house. I was about halfway through my chemotherapy, and I thought we were back in a relationship. He had been coming by taking care of me, and we had been intimate. He had called me earlier in the day to make sure I was coming to help him with his party, and I kind of felt like I was going to be 'the woman of the house.' When I got to his house, I noticed another woman there pretty much taking over the house. I didn't think anything of it because he has lots of family and friends. I mean, why would he have two women he was dating at the same party, right?!

Well, I saw her making up his bed and then I saw women and childrens clothing in the second bedroom. I realized this heffa had spent the night because the only reason you make up a bed is if you slept in it. Keep in mind, this is a man who always makes up his bed when he awakens each morning... unless someone was still in it after he got out of it. So, I went to him and asked who she was. "My ex-girlfriend came down from Flagstaff." I couldn't believe what I was hearing! So I say, "Did she spend the night?" He says, "Yes, she brought her kids, so they spent the night." I remember just wanting to sink through the floor! Why would he invite me knowing how I felt about him if he was gonna invite his EX-girlfriend? He had already told me that this EX continually calls him, tells him that she's in love with him, and wants to get back with him?! My head was pounding, and I could feel the Williams side of my bloodline pushing up (the side of my family that don't play).

I didn't know what to do. I was holding out hope that it was nothing, but as I walked past the kitchen, where she was clearly 'the woman of the house,' I heard her ask HIM who I was. He said, "my ex-girlfriend." I stopped because I wanted to listen to the rest of the conversation. She says, "Are you still seeing her?" I held my breath because, "YES, ASSHOLE! YOU ARE!" and he said, "No, we're just friends!" She then saw me standing there (he didn't), and she pulled him to the dance floor, where they started slow dancing, or should I say, having sex standing up, because that's what it looked like. I'm standing there, and his family, who knows me, is looking at me with pity. I was so humiliated! What an idiot I am! I just turned around, walked out the front door, and went home. I felt like the singer, Jazmine Sullivan – I wanted to Bust The Windows Out Of His Car!! I cried all night long. I called my best friend, Pam, to get her opinion. She was like, "Girl, you need to leave that negro alone. I have known you for fourteen years and never seen you cry over a man. He is not worth it." And I knew this, but the signals he had given all night were ridiculous. Several times, he would come up to me and caress my arm, hug me, ask me, "How are you doing, do you need anything?" So, what was I to think???

I cried all night – first because of what happened, then because he didn't call me to make sure I was okay, or to even apologize. I think I finally fell asleep at about five a.m., in a daze. The next day, at about three p.m., he called saying, "Hi, I'm calling everyone who came to my housewarming to thank them for coming. I've been calling people all morning."

WHAT THE ACTUAL FUCK?! You are calling me at three p.m. to say "Thank You!" and I'm the last on the list because you started calling early this morning!

I WAS TOO THROUGH!!

That flashback made me want to slam on the brakes. I pulled over to the side of the road and just put my head down on the steering wheel. I could feel myself getting angry all over again and wanting to cry. Only then, a little voice says, "What's wrong, Gramma?" THANK GOD! My granddaughter is with me! I had to pull myself together. I looked over at her with this big smile on my face. "Nothing, baby, I was just trying to remember how to get to the mall. You want to go buy some shoes or a purse?"

"YES, YES, YES – A Hello Kitty purse!" she says, bouncing up and down in the seat.

Good, because after that flashback, I'm gonna need another Louis Vuitton!!

Later that night, as I was taking all the stuff out of my "old" Louis Vuitton purse to put into my "new" Louis Vuitton purse, I was asking myself again "What is it about that asshole that you are really craving?", and the answer comes to me. He sucks me back in with the reminder of a brief flash of extreme exhilaration and the promise of affection and love. But, just like drugs, after that brief moment, they both kick you, stomp you, and leave you shivering and broken. You just want that moment of pleasure again, so you keep allowing the beatdown that you already know is coming back afterward.

Thank you, Jesus, for my flashback and my granddaughter. Otherwise, right now, I'd be on the verge of suicide.

Day 4: The Devil Is Blocking My Blessing

IT'S FIVE A.M., and time to get up and head to the airport. I have had a great time with my grandkids. I just wish I truly had been able to not work and spend so much time putting out so many fires. But that's part of being a REALTOR. We never have an entire day, let alone a whole week off. I guess I'd better accept and embrace that fact. Oh well, at least I made money while I was on vacation. It'll pay for all the money I spent in the last two weeks...

My grandkids were asleep, but I kissed their foreheads. These are the times I wished I still lived in Phoenix. I'd love to be closer to them so that I could watch them grow older. For a moment, my mind wandered into a daydream where I move back to Phoenix, HIM and I are together, happy, and building a future. I'm spending a couple of days a week with my grandbabies. Life is perfect.... But I snap back to reality because I remember that when I was living here, life with HIM was not perfect. But see, that's how it keeps you attached. The promise of bliss! He actually told me once that if I moved back to Phoenix, we would be back together, and everything would be perfect.

RIIIIGHT!!!

First of all, why do I need to move back to Phoenix for you to want to be with me?! If you love someone and want them as bad as you say you do, you'll deal with any obstacle and work it out. I mean, celebrities and millionaire businessmen live apart from their wives and girlfriends for weeks at a time. It's also a fact that often, men and women move to be with their loved ones all the time. If he loved and wanted to be with me, he would try. So stop trying to feed me that bullshit, I am not stupid. A five-hour distance should not be the issue that just prevents WHOLE relationships if you want to be with someone you SAY you love.

I know exactly what it is. He would love for me to move there and be his on-call booty call. I know the sex was awesome, and that's what he misses. But the knowledge that "he's just not that into me" is what's gonna keep my ass stepping to the airport and never looking back towards him.

I won't lie. I miss him, I want him, sometimes I ache for him. But fast forward, Girl…. Fast Forward!

It's funny, whenever I pray to God asking for HIM to be back in my life, God makes it PERFECTLY clear that "this one is not for you." I remember once that I was in the shower (I always pray in the shower), begging God to give HIM back to me. I swear on my kids I heard God say to me, "NO! NOT HIM!" So tell me, why do I ask for a word, then ignore the damn word or twist it up until it's what I want to hear?! Whenever we ask for a word or an answer, oh, we get it! It's just like when a woman's best friend tells her she saw her man on a cruise hugged up with another woman, even sends her a picture on her blackberry (after he told her he was going out of town on a business trip) and she STILL believes his ass when he says "It wasn't me!" What kind of stupid are we? (This actually happened, but since this is not her story, I won't name names) But…see… we're not stupid. Of course, she knew damn well that was her boyfriend, just like I know that was my answer from God. We just don't like THAT answer, so we act like we didn't get it. Talking about, "Oh, maybe that wasn't GOD, maybe it was the devil trying to block my blessing!" REALLY?!

One thing I do know, is that fool has not been a blessing in over five years. It's just time I let the fairytale go. Ain't no magic dust being sprinkled over me and HIM to make things right again.

HIM, just like crack cocaine, is never going to be good for me.

It's an illusion, a quick thirty-minute high before you fall back down. I once read a magazine article by a well-known psychologist, and Ph.D. (I can't remember her name) that says falling in love is like the high from smoking crack cocaine or shooting up with heroin. There are actual chemical changes in parts of the brain when you're in love that equals that of high heroin or cocaine doses. That's crazy!!

Now, let me get on the damn plane and get as far away from HIM…and, as quick as this plane can fly!

Day 5: Just Need A little Bit Of Lovin

I GOTTA ADMIT, I woke up this morning feeling kinda blue. I know it's pointless, but I still find myself trying to understand what can't be understood. I keep wondering how someone just keeps telling you how much they love you, how they can't imagine their future without you and then treat you like shit?! Okay, maybe not exactly 'like shit," but like they can take you or leave you. And to me…that's treating someone like shit. I'm a real, real honest person, so I can admit exactly what it is… I think he wants to break me!

You see, one of the things he always says to me is that "You are very, very, very spoiled." Okay, and????! What's wrong with that????!

First of all, I was very, very, very spoiled when you met me, you knew it from day one, and you participated. You treated me like a Queen, gave me everything I wanted, and didn't seem to have a problem with it then. But then, I in turn, treated you like a King!! I gave you everything you wanted, and whenever you wanted it. I brought you lunch to your job, bought you things just because. (Don't worry, ladies, I didn't buy big stuff, but you know, a shirt I thought would look good on him, sandals I wanted him to wear. You know, things to dress him up a bit.

Second of all, you're telling me that your priority is making money, not taking care of a woman and that you could never see yourself spoiling a woman. Three years after you've already been with "that woman" and treated her good?? It doesn't even make sense! Did you "Get Woke" 1,080 days after you were with me?! And what you call spoiling a woman, I call it being a man and treating a woman like a woman. Treating her like your queen, like you never want her to leave your side.

let me let you fellas in on a little secret, you wanna make sure your woman never even 'thinks' about leaving you? Then treat her better than she could ever conceive that another man would ever dream about treating her. I'm not talking about material things or buying her objects. I'm talking about making her feel like there's nothing you wouldn't do for her. Make her feel like you couldn't live without her, that you would do anything to see her smile, and that it would break your heart to see her cry. That's a "spoiled" woman. A woman just wants to feel like God took some time aside, just to create you for her and sent you from Heaven. That's it...you can keep your money! What you need to know is that a good woman is capable AND wants to make her own. It's not about what you actually can buy her, it's about what you WOULD buy her. Just the knowledge of the things you WOULD do for her overrides what you actually DO for her. All-day EVERY day!!

So get over the whole "You're so spoiled" thing. I've always said that I know my kids and grandkids are spoiled, but I love spoiling them. As long as they show a grateful spirit, I don't care how spoiled they are. And I have always shown a grateful spirit. Ask anyone!

Oh man, that felt good. Venting and ranting helps my recovery. As long as I remind myself of how HIM sloooowly destroys the essence of ME, and how that is not okay with my Father God, I can do this. (YASSS, I SO did just throw it on GOD!!)

Well, I had to get back to work. Talk about a distraction. I've got two Real Estate transactions to bring back from the brink of disaster. Real Estate can be exciting, but it is definitely not for the weak at heart. You can work with a Buyer or Seller for three months and finally secure a sale, then have it fall apart over something silly. I've seen Realtors break down crying. So now, I've gotta go save two. The person covering for me apparently had some sort of meltdown while I was gone. The Sellers, my Buyers, the Realtor on the other side of the deal, the Escrow Officer, AND some of the other Realtors in my office ALL called me while I was on my vacation telling me she was a Bitch to them. WTF??? Oh well, I'll get it handled. DO I HAVE A CHOICE??

First things first, I gotta talk to the Realtor covering for me to see what happened. So, I go to find her and ask, "Can I talk to you for a minute to get an update on my deals and what happened while I was gone?". I was just as sweet as pie (I do know how to be sweet sometimes). She blows right by me, saying "I'm super busy right now, I have a lot of fires I'm putting out. I can't talk to you now!"

HUNH???!

I'm just standing there wondering what is REALLY going on. I need to know what's going on with my shit, and you "don't have time?!" So I just started calling my folks directly to find out what happened. I am not in the mood to lose my job for punching this heffa in the throat before I get my commission check.

First, I call my Buyer. She's upset and says, "I know the person covering for you is your friend, but she was a total bitch to me!" WOW!!

All I can do is apologize to my Buyer client and assure her that she doesn't have to do anything she doesn't want to do. If she wants to cancel, we will cancel! But she calms down and decides not to cancel. She's 23 (a kid), and her dad was in the hospital. All she needed was someone to hold her hand a bit and explain the process of signing loan documents gently, not harshly. But she's good now, happy, and ready to close the deal. YES!!

Ironically, she starts telling me that amid all this stress, she'd decided that her boyfriend wasn't the one for her, and she broke up with him. What? Something must be in the water. I told her, "Honey, I don't want to minimize what you're going through, because I'm going through the same thing right now. But one thing I do know is that if someone can't love you the way you want them to love you, you owe it to yourself to move on. Life is too short, and every day we wake up to enjoy another day that God has blessed us with. We CANNOT disrespect God's blessings by wasting ANOTHER second on someone that doesn't deserve us. You're a GREAT catch. Hell, you're only 23 years old, have a good job, a SUPER healthy bank account, and buying a home by yourself!" The poor thing started crying and says, "But I loved him and was with him for three years. I don't understand." I feel like I'm talking to myself. But, I check my smart ass mouth and just say, "I know, I get it. But you should love yourself more than you love him and if you do, you'll realize that he can't love you. If he did, he could not bear to see you hurting and would do anything to prevent it. You'll be okay – you're young, beautiful, and have your own condo now. Do NOT let him eat if he's not bringing anything to the table! Dammit, he should be bringing the WHOLE table!"

After my conversation with her, I'm sitting there, and I realize how we always think it's just us struggling with this shit, but soooo many people go through this love addiction. We either don't want to or can't move on and get out of it. So, we either keep going back to these jerks, or we find a new jerk just like the last one. I used to wonder why celebrities struggle so long and hard to make it, FINALLY get famous, start having the money and fame they desired for so long, and they STILL do drugs?! I mean, I don't wonder why they start. I get that, most of them are young when they start. They've just got more money than sense. They just want to party, then skeezy lowlife drug dealers intentionally give them drugs for free so they'll get hooked. But I always thought, "Go to rehab, stop, get your great life back." But now I see that it's not that easy. I mean, it's easy to say, "this sucks, and I quit you!" But it's not easy to STAY "Quitted." You get depressed and lonely. Then, you start thinking your best, most fun times were when you were in that high. And now, your reality sucks. You start to sink lower and lower.

Drug addicts break down and say, "I'm just gonna smoke a little/drink a little. I won't let it get out of control." Love addicts say, "I'm just gonna call him; just go get me some. I'm gonna control this, let him know I don't need him, that I just want a hit and run for the night." Well, my friends, I'm here to tell you That's Bullshit!!! We're all fooling ourselves. Once that hook is under our skin, we're gone for God knows how long – but in the end, it's the same. We're left huddling under the comforter crying, can't eat, can't think, and just wanting to take a nose dive off the 57/10 freeway exchange.

Ok, back to work...LORD... I MUST find a distraction. My mind is going places I don't want it to go. But, of course, since everybody knows I went to Phoenix and that HIM lives there, I'm asked all day, "Did you see him? Are you moving there with him?" All the questions that I want to say yes to. But I just smile and say, "I spent most of my time with my grandchildren," knowing DAMN well....

Sidebar - Why is there always so much drama in the workplace with women? I mean, that's why I love working with and hanging out with men (once you get past them thinking they're getting some), they don't come at you messy. Women can be so petty, "She thinks she's cute, she thinks she's the bomb, she thinks she dresses cute, I don't know HOW she was selected for the Assistant Manager position"... It goes on and on. Guess what, Heffa??? – You have another THANK coming... But, it's all good... See – taking my kindness and good nature for weakness is your BIG mistake...I wonder how long it will take you to realize that the information I just gave you is WRONG, and your file is about to be rejected??? Perhaps when you can't get your commission check???!!! Hmmmph.

Okay, yes, that was ugly. I'll pray about that because GOD does NOT LIKE UGLY, and I refuse to let some Has Been Realtor block my blessings.

But see, that's why this recovery process is sooooo hard. My mind is on HIM, work stress, kid stress, health stress, family stress, and then this nonsense stress. So, at the end of the day, you're so tempted to say, "I just need a little bit of lovin', I'll just call HIM. It's just a phone call, what harm can it do?" And then, you start fantasizing, thinking "he probably misses me as much as I miss him. He just doesn't know how to say it to me because he's so prideful."

And, just like that...HIM has crept into my mind and under my skin again... Now, I can't even think straight. I feel myself withdrawing into the sickness. I'm shaking, but I'm not a scary person. It's like that song R&B singer Jazmine Sullivan sings, "I'm not scared of lions, or tigers, or bears...but I'm scared of...loving you." Right now, I feel like a dead man walking, can't even focus.

I gotta get out of here... I'm rambling.

I read somewhere that a big part of recovering from an addiction is figuring out your triggers, learning what happens that all of a sudden throws you into a tailspin and makes you feel like you HAVE to have it???!!! Once you figure that out, you can manage it better because you can avoid the triggers. That's what I haven't figured out yet – all the triggers. But, I do know that right now, I'm sinking into self-pity. Why am I so weak when it comes to him? By all accounts, I'm strong, I'm intelligent, I'm hard-working, I'm attractive, I'm funny. What is it about ME – that I can't just drop that habit like a hot potato?? I can point out so many things about him that should make me throw up in my mouth. But right now, I can't think of anything else except how much I want to at least hear his voice. Just hearing his voice can't hurt anything, can it? How can I be so strong everywhere else and so weak for this man???!! Is it my own pride and arrogance? Am I so vain that the thought that a man may not want ME is unacceptable to MY ego? Could this be true? What kind of madness is that? I need to put some serious thought into this.

Later, I'm at home, just chilling. I don't have to wake up early tomorrow, so an Ambien is what I need tonight since I couldn't find anything else to ease my mind. Thirty minutes later, my cell phone is ringing off the hook. I'm sure it's work-related, but this Ambien has me so far down the rabbit hole that I can't even think about talking about Real Estate.

I drifted off to sleep thinking about not just HIM, but about US. Tears streaming down my face, and I realized that I DIDN'T call him today….and that's a bittersweet thought…

Uggghh, this detox is KILLING me…

Day 6: Don't Wanna Be In The 2nd Book

AFTER SLEEPING in until about ten a.m., I rolled out of bed to take a shower. It was a good, restful sleep with no crazy dreams. That Ambien helped a lot, it prevented my usual tossing and turning. I think I'll take a "ME" day, and then spend the day with one of my best friends. Someone who's ALWAYS positive, fun, and who's always willing to do what I want to do – ME!!! I'm my Best Friend, I am She! Hahaha. I happen to look down at my hands and realize that my nails are looking a hot mess, so I'll start with them today.

I stepped outside, and LORD, it is such a beautiful day today! This is why people flock to Southern California.

Halfway through the day, I started thinking that one of the problems with ME hanging out with myself is that I obsess about the same love addiction issues over and over. So, I'm not a good distraction for myself, and a distraction is what I need. But, my retail therapy is working pretty good. My recent vacation with my kids and grandkids was great, but I always focus so much on them that I forget about ME. I'm gonna make that up to me right away by starting with a #5 mani/pedi, you know, the expensive one! A girl's gotta keep up with those toes, or you'll end up with bear claws, and that is NOT a good look.

Forty-five minutes later, I head over to get a massage. There's a guy at the place next to Verizon in Chino that knows how to make your Twiddle twaddle... I'm just saying!!!

OH MY GOD!!!! YASSS!!

I needed those knots worked out. I think I need a massage weekly, forget that monthly crap. My life is waaaay too complicated for a monthly massage to help me at all. I feel rather good heading out of the massage parlor, so I figure I'll drop in at Lucille's BBQ in Chino Hills for a nice Salmon Caesar Salad. As soon as I head towards Chino Hills Parkway, my cell phone starts to blow up. I reach down to answer it, look at the number, and it's like someone threw a glass of ice-cold water in my face!!!

WHY CAN'T HE LEAVE ME ALONE???!!!

Oh, God, it's a serious dilemma. I feel like I'm an alcoholic at a restaurant, and someone accidentally ordered me a Jack on The Rocks when it was just supposed to be a coke. It looks so good, the Alcoholic realizes what it is, and is tempted to have a small sip because they're sure it won't be that bad this time. Maybe this time, you can just have the one, and Jack Daniels will realize that he truly wants you in his life forever and not use, abuse, and kick you to the curb, right??!!

But, that's not what's really gonna happen, is it? We all know where that one small drink will lead an Alcoholic...

So, do I answer? Do I not??

It took me so long to think about answering the phone that the call went to voicemail. I don't even want to listen to the message...So, I don't. I drove on over to Lucille's. I can't even wait to sit down to order a drink. The hostess says, "how many?" Shit, I just place my order with her – "One Jack Daniels Mint Julep in the bar, please, extra shot of Jack, easy on the ice and whatever else you put in there!"

A few sips later, and I can think straight. I don't know how people go through this shit and keep their sanity!! It makes you NEVER want to get into another relationship! DAMN!! But, let me get this over with. So, I listen to the voicemail message, because we all know that I'm eventually going to listen to it, so I might as well get it over with.

"Hey there, "HIM" here. I just wanted to hear your voice, so I guess I'll just have to be satisfied with your voicemail. I want to make sure you're alright. Guess I'll talk to you later."

WTF???!!

Now, what do I do with that shit???

"Waiter, can I get another Jack Daniels Mint Julep, please??....and, hold the ice."

I think these damn men got E.S. Damn P.!!

As soon as they think you MIGHT be able to move on, they pop the fuck back up!!

GONE ON WITH THAT B.S.!!!!

But at least there's no danger of me calling him back. He's got me so pissed off that the mere THOUGHT of calling him makes me want to throw this drink at the man sitting down the bar from me.

I'm getting ready to take my drunk ass home and sign up for Match.com like my friend has been telling me to do. I gotta do something to get over HIM faster. He's damn near made me lose my Christianity today – got me cussing like a sailor! How am I gonna get in the Pearly Gates like this??!! St. Peter will be like, "girl, get on from here. You are in the Second Book!!"

I guess I'll tell Saint Peter, "Well, what had happened was....."

Didn't even get my damn Salmon Caesar Salad!!

Day 7: Match.com Or Nah?

LORD, Jesus… I cannot drink like I used to!

I only had two Mint Juleps last night, and I am hungover!! Well, I did get extra shots of Jack Daniels, and they were BIG drinks.

But, I am gonna get up and go to church. All I remember about last night is every other word out of my mouth was a curse word. That is NOT cool. Let me get on to church. One question – Why are black churches ALWAYS a three-hour session? Does GOD say more to black pastors than to other races?? I'm just saying…But, I need my word from GOD today, and I may actually need four hours today.

Church was awesome. The Pastor and Minister were on fire today!! I did go up to the Pastor during service and ask him to remove this anger I have in my heart for HIM. The negativity is taking up valuable space, and I'm tired OF and FROM it. I accept that I have a ways to go to be "over" HIM, but I can't let this eat me up.

But, ugh, I did sign up for Match.com last night. It was kinda like me drunk dialing somebody though. I'm sure my profile will scare men off. It reads like this:

"I'm a decently smart and hard-working woman

with what I think is a wicked sense of humor. Of course, my children don't agree. I have four children - all grown or away at college. I'm not sure what type of relationship I want, but I do know that I want to start with GREAT companionship and someone with the same values as I have (which I believe will become evident over time). I am not interested in dating a man with minor children, and I do not care to date men who smoke…even if you only smoke socially – whatever that is"

I checked my e-mail when I got home from Church. WHY did I have five winks! After the profile I posted? What's wrong with these men? I didn't think one man would want to even read the whole thing.

So, I called my friend, Marilyn, who told me to join in the first place. "I have five winks, what am I supposed to do with that?" She cracked up laughing. "What's so funny? I wasn't telling a joke," I asked her. Actually holding back my own laughter, cause the whole situation WAS kind of funny. Why am I fifty years old and don't know what to do when someone winks at me?? LOL.

"Girl, you read their profiles, and if he seems the LEAST bit interesting, you wink back. And, if you're REALLY interested and think you'd want to go out with him, you e-mail him," Marilyn managed to get out. How, I don't know, because she was still cackling at me…Cackling Ass.

LORD! This is waaay too much!

"But, how do I know if they're not sexual predators, or murderers, or deadbeats with no jobs AND bad credit? I wanted to know.

Marilyn's wise advice was, "well, that's why you have a conversation by e-mail for a while before you give him your phone number. Or don't even give him your phone number. Take his phone number or e-mail address and make a daytime coffee date with him after you feel comfortable."

LORD! Again, this is too much!!

But, I decide it can't hurt to wink back at a few. Besides, I've watched enough episodes of "Criminal Minds" to know what to watch out for. And, one misstep, and they are O-U-T.

Most of these men are a HOT MESS!! Why are you damn near sixty years old with two and three-year-old children?? My LAST baby is almost sixteen years old, and I'm counting the months to eighteen. I am NOT trying to start over again, playing mommy. I know it's just dating, but what if we really start liking each other a lot?? Hunh! It ain't happening.

So, I find three of them that appear to be possibilities, and I wink back at them. Now, I guess I sit back a few days to see what happens. At least this will give me a HUGE distraction from HIM!!

I look outside and notice that it's another beautiful day in Southern California. I decided to go to Albertson's grocery store and buy some marinated chicken breasts, a package of Farmer Johns Hot Links, and some sweet corn on the cob. I got a little grill (just big enough for a couple of people) and have a taste for all of that. Plus, I'll have some food left for tomorrow.

Oh, wait!! Let me grab some of my business cards. They have a business board at Albertsons. I might get a little Real Estate business – It's all about Face Recognition!!

Once I get to the store, I go directly to the board, and at first, I'm thrilled. I left five cards the last time I was here, and now they're all gone. But, as I think about it, I realize that I haven't received any calls or leads related to the cards I left. I start thinking, "Who in the ENTIRE Hell took my five business cards?" You know, I tend to be a bit paranoid, so now I'm thinking that either some other scandalous Realtor took them down, or some pervert took them. Because, if another Realtor took them, wouldn't I see her/his business cards up there? And, if a real potential client took them, wouldn't I have received at least a couple of phone calls by now??

Hmmmmmmmph....

Anyways, I get my food and go on home....looking over my shoulder, under the car and in the back seat...just in case.

After I boil my hot links and corn for a little while and light the grill (why is that so difficult?? They need to make a grill for single women, where you just throw in the coals, a match or turn the knob, and it's on. All this making sure the fire stays lit is for the birds), I sit down with a glass of wine and just relax.

While my food is cooking on the grill, my Blackberry starts singing "My Prerogative" – the Britney Spears version. That's how I know that I have new e-mails. I check my e-mail, and I have three. One from each of the men I winked back at on Match.com!!

Oh LORD, what do I do with this now???!!!

So, I call Marilyn, yet AGAIN, "Girl, all three men I winked back at e-mailed me. What do I do now??" Marilyn asks me, "Is someone in the room with you?"...odd question. I was like, "Nooooo, why?" Marilyn cracks up, laughing again. I guess I'm the joke today!!! She says, "then, why are you whispering?" I hadn't even realized that I was whispering!! I then notice that I'm all hunched over the phone, with one hand partially covering it and that I AM whispering.

"Okay, Okay, Okay, just tell me what I'm supposed to do now," I said. "What did their e-mail say?" she asked me. Damn, I hadn't even read the darn things yet. Marilyn tells me to read them to her with her nosy ass. They all pretty much start with the same Bullshit – "how attractive you are, blah, blah, blah." Don't try to butter me up, that's probably the same line they use with every other desperate heffa.

Ewwwww, nasty mofo's – one of them actually says in the e-mail that he would like to make me feel good sexually and knows many ways to do just that. Okay, though that may be something appropriate for my boyfriend to whisper softly in my ear, this is too much…way too much, and way too soon, Bro!! I was gonna just delete him, but then I thought, "let me help this brother out." So, I typed **"Ewww. If you're trying to turn women off, keep sending these types of e-mails. If you're trying to meet a woman of quality – waaaay too much, waaaay too soon. Again, Ewww!"** Then….I deleted his ass!!!

The next guy seemed decent. Fifty years old, lives in Newport Beach, says he's just trying to meet friends and if it leads to more, great. He says that he liked the honesty of my profile, was intrigued by it, and "nice photos." Would I like to perhaps meet for coffee? The only problem? This mofo has a three-year-old son!! But, as Marilyn keeps telling me, "you ain't' trying to marry out the gate. Just meet him, and at the worst, you get a few free meals!" She's right, and one thing about me – I don't turn down no free meal, a girl's gotta eat. So, I e-mailed him back: "Thanx for the compliment, and I would love to meet you for coffee someday." I mean, he seemed respectful, was over six feet tall, looked handsome from his photos, so I was a little excited.

He e-mailed me back later that evening and set a coffee date for the next day, 8:30 a.m. at Panera Bread in Chino Hills. Nice and open with many other restaurants and people around.

I fell asleep that night, hopeful, and I did not think about or dream about HIM.

This could be good.

Day 8: Internet Dating...THE LIES!!

I WAKE up kind of excited, no thoughts or dreams of HIM, and hopeful for this breakfast date. Don't get me wrong, not hopeful that "he's The One," or that I've met my soulmate that I'll marry in six months. I'm excited because I've begun a new journey, and that I'm finally going to be able to move on. I decided to dress Sexy Professional since I have to go to work afterward. So, I put on my brown knit dress that my ex-husband says makes him want to "do me" whenever he sees me in it, and my multi-color five-inch pumps. Not the CFM (Google that) ones, the ones "women" like too.

Hair still looking good – you know, that Brazilian virgin bouncing around (haha). It's not a DATE, date. So, toned down makeup, but a little more on the eyes than I'd normally do for work.

I get to Panera Bread about fifteen minutes early and sit in a booth facing the door. I need to be able to see this mofo AHEAD of time! So, I'm sitting there in anticipation, getting a bit excited, and Benny walks up to me. Wait, that's not Benny, but a dead ringer for him. Now, let me tell you who Benny is. Benny is my manager's husband, and I love Benny to pieces. But, this lying yahoo said he was fifty, six foot four, about 200 pounds and fit.

This fool was at least 68 years old; he was about six foot four inches. But, if he considered himself "fit," then you can consider Ruben Studdard anorexic, and the eight strands of hair on his head were white.

WTF?

As he kept walking towards me, with the gait of Jerry (my twelve-year-old arthritic, bad hipped Golden Retriever), it was all I could do NOT to bolt out the side door. But, I knew that would be a challenge with my five inch high heels. OOOOH, I wish I had on my sneakers right now. My ass would be in Pomona now, I'd be running so fast. I can't believe this shit!

I'm in shock, but I'm a fairly decent actress (like most wives, mothers, and Real Estate Agents have learned to be), so I just smiled at him and said hello. He's grinning like a kid in a candy store as he eases his decrepit, old ass bones in the chair. He says, "You sure are pretty. You look much better in person than in your profile pictures." "Uh, Thanx," I mumbled. Because I'm still in shock. We make small talk for a while; I don't even know about what. He asks me if I was hungry and would I like to go up to order anything to eat. Of course, I've now lost my damn appetite. But, I said, "yes, thank you, maybe coffee and a light breakfast," I don't want to appear to be ALL the way rude, and as we've already established, I don't turn down no free meals! We got up to go to the front counter, and I swear I hear his damn bones cracking! Daaaaammmn! But, I just tell myself, "Self, see the shit through. At least it's a free breakfast."

"My date" starts reviewing the menu and says, "WOW! This place is a little pricey." Now, I'm damn near speechless and willing myself NOT to run out the door. It's not that he could catch me with his old ass.

Are you serious???!! Panera Bread?? Too pricey?? Not for a grown-ass man on a first date who claims he owns his own

Internet Technology Company. I mean, coffee and a breakfast sandwich are less than $10! I don't want to break his ass, so I just order a coffee and a muffin. He just gets coffee.

We sat down, and I can't say a word, but he seems to be comfortable and happy and just starts talking. "So, Kayla, how long have you been on Match?" "Not long," I manage to get out. Already thinking TOO DAMN LONG!! "How about you?" I inquire. He leans back, looks toward the sky, placing his hands over his six-month pregnant belly, and says, "Oh, about eight months." And, I am curious, so I ask, "And?" "Well," he says, "I've gone out on many first dates but haven't met 'that one' yet."

NO SHIT, SHERLOCK!! Why don't we start with the fact that your profile says your fifty, and I know damn well your ass is at least sixty-eight! Your profile also says your physique is tall and average build, with you working out several times a week. If this shit is average, I'm anorexic and about to fall over! And, let's not even get on the "working out several times a week part??" Working what out? – your hand to mouth activity?? This man is truly delusional.

See, right now, I'm starting to crave HIM. This is some B.S.

I guess I must have been looking at my date kind of crazy, or he can tell something is off. He says, "You know, I may as well be honest about some things because I didn't expect you to look so young and good in person. No one from Match typically looks as good as their pictures, and you look better."

Okay, this is getting interesting. "Thanx," I say. "What did you want to tell me?" as I lean towards him, curious now and wanting to hear what he has to say.

Well, you might not be able to tell, but I'm not fifty. I'm closer to sixty," He pauses for effect. You know, I'm not a mean person. I mean, yeah, I have a quick and deadly bite like a rattlesnake when someone pisses me off and deserves it, but I'm not one to be mean just to be hurtful. But, I feel like I was misled and made to waste my time. So, at that moment, I feel that maybe I can save him some time in future dates cuz his old ass sure don't have a lot of time left. So, I take a deep breath and say to him, "You know, can I be honest with you?" He looks a little panicked, but smiles and says, "Please do."

With another deep breath, I start... "First of all, you seem like a nice guy, but it's quite obvious that you lied about your age. I think you're closer to sixty-five years old. Don't get me wrong, you look good for sixty-five, but if you describe yourself a certain way, then show up entirely different, it's not gonna set the tone for a good date. Women would already be thinking, 'LIAR.' And then, on top of that, you're nothing like you described on your profile. Obviously, your profile pictures are old. I just think you have to be honest about who you are because women are describing exactly what they want, and that's what they expect to show up. If I said on my profile that the maximum age I will consider is fifty-five, it's pretty disrespectful for someone over sixty-five to show up without full disclosure and letting me know upfront. Who knows, I may still decide to meet you, but give ME that option and choice. Don't just show up."

At this point, he's pretty speechless but says, "Damn, and I knew my three-year-old son would really like you. You kind of look like his mother."

I gotta get the hell out of here.

I got up and walked out.

For the first time in ten days, I had a good laugh. I laughed for the rest of the day.

That was for damn sure a good distraction!!

Day 9: Ambien And A Glass of Wine

WHY IS it that friends with no man always want to give you "relationship" advice? That's not advice, that's your damn opinion based on your own misguided experiences. The only people whose advice I'll even listen to is someone who's currently in or HAD been married for thirty plus years. Hell, I was in a marriage for more than eighteen years and wouldn't give NOBODY love or marriage advice. As you can see, I'm still struggling with that concept. And if you ask me about love and marriage today, I'm gonna say, "you're a damn fool for considering either!"

You know, I'm still confused about these youngsters wanting to get married so early. Kids, other than them Social Security benefits later, it ain't all that you think it is. I understand that you want what you THINK your other married friends have. But, what you're really going to get is the right to be misled for the day that took six to twelve months to get to, caused you to lose at least two good friends because you couldn't ask them all to be in the wedding, the day that cost $10,000 or more, that gave you at least two ulcers because "something" went wrong or "somebody" felt the need to approach the bride or groom about what they thought was going wrong with the day. Then after all that, you didn't at least get decent sex because his/her drunk ass passed out. YOU WANT THAT DAY???!!!

And, THEN, you get to spend another $20,000 to get rid of his/her sorry ass when you finally "SEE" his/her trifling ass. AND LET'S NOT EVEN TALK ABOUT IF YOU HAVE CHILDREN WITH HIS DEADBEAT ASS!!!

I'm just saying…

I get fighting for rights that you've earned by being with someone for years, but that's called palimony.

Unless you have the opportunity to marry Denzel, Oprah, or Ellen DeGeneres… WELL, NOW THAT'S JUST DIFFERENT…I would fight for that marriage too.

I thought about HIM today. I was at the mall, minding my own damn business, and noticed a couple that reminded me of US at the beginning of our relationship.

FLASHBACK: HIM called me on a gorgeous Saturday morning, "what are your plans today?" I was just lounging around that day, so I was thrilled to hear his voice. His voice is so sexy, and he was usually so considerate. I knew something special was on his mind. "My plans were to lie around thinking about you, and getting excited about the thought of being with you sometime today," I softly purred into the phone. See, because that's the stage we were at in our relationship. Saying teasing, pleasing things to each other all the time.

Purring and shit.

"Well," he says, "I was thinking I'd take you shopping and buy you some clothes."

HUNH???!!

Now, obviously, it's not as if men haven't bought or given me many expensive items in or with the hopes of a relationship. But, no one had ever just called out of the blue and said, "I want to take you

shopping." Especially after only 2 months into the relationship. At that point, we hadn't even discussed exclusivity or being each other's "boyfriend and girl-friend." So, I was surprised. Pleasantly, but surprised nonetheless.

He picked me up from my house, we went to the Metro Center Mall off the 17 Freeway (back when it was a nice mall) and had a fantastic day. We went from store to store, he picked out outfits that he liked, I tried them on, and I let him make the final selections. I think he bought me eight outfits that day. It was awesome. He didn't do it because I didn't have clothes (I have waaay too many clothes, which those who know me can testify to) or because he thought I was broke (he didn't, and I wasn't). But, I think he did it because he believed it's the kind of thing men do for their women. He also had his idea of what he wanted to see me in...and he had excellent taste!!

And this kind of memory is again what makes it so hard to move on and let it go. What or who else can make you feel so good, even if only for a fleeting moment? I'm telling you, drug addicts don't want to be drug addicts, but they think about that moment that felt soooooo... sighhhh.

Let me go pass out some business cards. I have got to stay busy because the desire to call HIM is overwhelming right now.

Maybe if I just keep reminding myself that it wouldn't be another love connection...There I go again, starting to justify ways to have a little bit of HIM back in my life. I'm thinking that I can still see him sometime and have the fun part, the feel-good part and protect my heart. I can maybe date a few men, including him. That way, I won't fall in love with him again.... But, that's a problem. That's the disease of addiction whispering in my ear again. It's like a crack addict who's trying to convince themselves that they can do crack "sometimes," and that they won't let it control them again.

FOR REAL, FOR REAL???!!!

Yes, it will!!! It will grab me, consume me, devour me. And then, I'll be hooked on him again. I have to remember that I am addicted to HIM and that I am powerless if I don't control that.

I HAVE TO MOVE ON!!!

I took an Ambien (yes, again!!!), drank a glass of red wine, and immersed myself in an episode of "Snapped."

As I drifted off to sleep, I thought I heard HIM's voice... calling out my name...

Day 10: They're Not Always Your friend

I WOKE up this morning with an ultra-clear mind and a smile on my face. I know I had a dream, but I don't remember what. I hope it was about a new life, with a new man, and not the same old shit. But, I don't have a whole lot of time to trip about that. I've gotta get dressed and get to work. My staff meeting starts in an hour and then I've gotta get to work on some new business. The sales transactions that I was working on when I left for vacation are all closed, and I've got to get some new leads. Plus, today, I think I'll find out exactly what my co-worker's damn issue was while I was on vacation. She was supposed to cover for me and obviously didn't since I was on the phone and computer every damn day putting out fires. The last time I tried to talk to her about it, she blew me off. I wasn't going to say anything else to her since it all got handled, but some of my other co-workers have been making odd comments like "you know, she's not REALLY your friend," "how do you pick your partners? you may want to find another vacation coverage method," and "next time you go on vacation, I'll cover for you." There's some shit going on, and I guess I'm gonna have to handle it. It's starting to feel like middle school, and I'm too old for this shit.

Walking into my office in Chino Hills, I can feel excitement and a buzz in the air. People are working!!! They are selling homes, and they are NOT playing. I can tell the difference since the Diamond Ranch office merged with the Chino Hills office. It's like the Diamond Ranch transplants have something to prove, and the Chino Hills O.G.'s are staking their claim to their territory. It's all good, though. It'll keep everyone on their toes. Competition is healthy for all salespeople.

So, I do see my co-worker that had covered for me while I was on vacation. Before I can say anything, she actually says to me, "I need to talk to you about something that's been bothering me." I'm surprised, but it's okay because it's what I needed too. We go into her office, I close the door and sit down and say, "what's up?" I'm genuinely perplexed at her attitude towards me lately. She doesn't look in my eyes, but finally says, "I wanted to talk to you because I've been upset about a couple of things lately and it's been bothering me." I sat back in the chair and said, "Yeah, I've noticed that. What's UP?" I could tell she didn't know how to get it out, but I'm still irritated about how she dropped the ball when she was supposed to be covering for me while I was on vacation. So I just let her stumble her way through it. "Well, I'm upset with you because James told me you had taken a client that he referred to me two years ago."

WTF???!!!

I must have looked like a complete idiot because I didn't know what the HELL she was talking about and certainly DID NOT expect that to come out of her mouth!! Finally, after what seemed like an hour (and I'm sure it was only a few seconds), I sputtered out, "I have abso..fucking..lutely no idea what or who you're talking about!!! What client and when?? No one named James has EVER referred a client to me!!!"

She just gave me an incredulous look, like I was lying. "I

think his name was Jose," she finally says. I was like, "hunh?" I guess I must have sat there for thirty full seconds before it hit me!! "Jose??" I whispered. "Jose is a tax client that James referred to me two years ago! He had a short sale before I ever met him, so I helped him with his taxes. He couldn't even buy a house, and that was NEVER a part of our conversation. Are you serious??!!" Finally, I'm screaming. Dumb ass just looks at me with the stupidest look on her face. "Oh, I didn't know." I have to take a breath before I answer because I can see the red fog coming over my eyes that happens whenever I'm about to GO THE HELL OFF. But, I don't want my manager to hear me, and we're right next to her office. So, I take another breath, like I'm in labor – hee hee ooh, hee hee ooh. I speak very slow and clear to make sure she understands. "You know, first of all, I don't need to steal a lead. What's for me is for me, and I will get mine. Second, if James told you this TWO years ago, I'm concerned that you've been holding on to this for two WHOLE years, pretending that we're cool. So, that means you are a fake. And, lastly, why did you conveniently let this bother you while I was on vacation but AFTER you took your vacation!!??" I just got up to leave the office, I was TOO threw. AS I walked out the door, I turned around and said: "And, I WILL call James to clear this up with him!"

REALLY???!!! DO I NEED THIS GRADE SCHOOL SHIT IN MY LIFE???!!

I'M ABOUT TO CALL IT A DAY!!

At 9:30 p.m., my craving was back. I should not have had that third vodka and pineapple juice. I want to call HIM so bad. I'm re-living those five hour nights of intimacy, waking up to a near orgasm, showering together, and then spending the day watching Sex & The City re-runs while he massaged my feet. Jesus, what was I thinking when I let him go??

I should just call him now! I know he wants me back!
SHIT, SHIT, SHIT!!!! I cannot!!

So, I decided to take a drug that's not as bad as crack or heroin…Some would consider it Methadone. I call it my ex-husband. Yes!! I made a booty call.

Day 11: The Walk Of Shame

DAMN!! My head is pounding, and my eyes are glued together...

WTF??!!

Did I fall asleep with my contacts in? I roll over in my bed...OH Shit!!

Shit, Shit, Shit!!!

THIS AIN'T MY BED!!!

I am lying next to my ex-husband, naked. It's all coming back to me now – making that call, going to his house, the shots of chocolate Patron, and an entire night of serious sex. Evidently, the sex was serious because my whole body is sore and my thighs ache.

Ugggghh...I don't even know how to feel. On the one hand, I did call him, and I knew what I wanted when I called. On the other hand, I know this is opening up a door that he won't understand was a "I just want it when I need it" door. I know that's wrong, but it's the truth. He's going to think I want some type of relationship or that he can call me whenever HE wants sex. The real deal is that I just wanted physical sex because my craving for HIM was out of control last night. Because even if I allow myself to just hear HIS voice, I will relapse – to the point of disaster. Having sex with my ex-husband was a distraction that gave me one more day of not thinking of HIM, but it does not make me feel good about myself.

I slowly and quietly start to get out of bed and grab my clothes so I can get out of there before he wakes up.

I feel sick to my stomach. I wish I hadn't drank that tequila, but without drinking that, I wouldn't have slept with him, and I needed to "de-stress" myself.

Jesus, help me! By the time I get HIM out of my system, I will be a straight alcoholic!!

Sneaking down the stairs, it hits me again – I AM DOING THE WALK OF SHAME. THIS IS NOT A GOOD LOOK!!

2 P.M.

I'm waking up with a splitting headache, and the sun is beaming in my eyes. For a moment, I don't even know where I am, but the minute I remember, I groan. My whole body is sore, not to mention the fact that my head is pounding like you wouldn't believe. Today is gonna be a "stay in bed," not "answer the phone" day. I start to feel the old familiar regret, but I squash that shit imee-jitt-ly! What good would it do? I made my decision, did what I did, I'm a grown-ass woman – it is what it is. Besides, it worked! I didn't think about HIM for a while. I would rather have mindless, "no fear of falling back in love with you" sex than falling back into the "no future" trap with HIM.

I could have done without drinking so much, but no way I would have had sex with my ex-husband without some serious libations.

Thinking of HIM, all I can think is "Damn HIM!"

And then I drift off back to sleep for the evening. The best thing to do about a hangover (other than keep drinking) is just sleep it off – I won't need an Ambien tonight.

Day 12: Best Distraction Ever

I WOKE up with a start and with my heart beating about 100 miles an hour. I had to calm myself down and slow my breathing. For a few minutes, I couldn't figure out why I woke up like that. Then, the memories hit me like a Mack truck. I dreamed of HIM...not the bad stuff...the good stuff – the happy times. I dreamed of us going to a nightclub and dancing. Just hugged up, bodies close, and only having eyes for each other. Our friends telling us how "sickening" it was the way we acted like we were the only two in the room. DO YOU KNOW HOW GOOD IT FEELS TO BE TOLD THAT YOUR RELA- TIONSHIP WITH YOUR MAN IS SICKENING???!! LOL... Memories of us singing that Mary J. Blige and Wyclef Jean song, "911" – **"someone please call 911, I just been shot down...with a bullet, in the heart."** THAT feeling of utter ecstasy – better than any drug you could ever have. Then I woke up...

I rolled over for a few more minutes of sleep. I slept for about thirty more minutes, feeling a LITTLE more refreshed, positive, and excited about my day. I should be getting my commission check for my Mercer Street closing, and I'm going to get my new computer today. Damn, I think I might go ahead and get my massage AND those COACH flats today. WOW!! I am so blessed! I know THE DRUG (Him) is there, but I'm not craving it AT THIS MOMENT. I wish I could say I don't even think about it, and I don't want it, but I'd be lying. I think about him, and I still want a part of HIM, but I know that he doesn't treat me right, and I deserve better.

Usually, it takes me about fifteen minutes to roll out of bed, but this morning I hopped out like a three-year-old running to wake up my mommy for some Cheerios. Standing in front of the bathroom mirror, I'm not too, too happy about my stomach pooch, but it ain't bad for a fifty-year-old grandma. Once I get my new boobs, start playing golf and belly dancing for about a month, I'll be (as my sixteen-year-old son says) "what you want!" But I am going to have Dominique put a few more tracks in my head. My hair is a little thin. I'm still thinking it's a little long for my lifestyle, but if Dominique says I can "rock it," I'm giving it another week. I just don't want to look unprofessional. I'm trying to be a Real Estate Rockstar with a diverse client base, and I don't want to look like a video hoochie. I'm just saying. Well, let me get on to the office.

About 2 p.m. –

I wasn't sure what mall to go to. The Shoppes In Chino Hills needs more stores, Montclair Mall needs some serious updating, and Brea Mall seems soo damn far. "Stop being so lazy, girl!!!" knowing twenty minutes ain't gonna kill me. Got my check, so – some money in my purse. After how I woke up, I just need to shake that out of my system. "They" (whoever the hell "they" are) say the best way to get over someone is to get under someone else, but I gotta tell you, buying a new purse sure helps too.

And then, my phone is starting to ring off the hook. Why is it, my ex-husband??!!

LORD, why did I re-start this mess with him???!!!! I wish I was more like a guy – able to just be with someone for the sex.

Swing by their house, get mine, wake up, go home and not give it a second thought....just call you when I get horny again.

But, I gotta admit – it might just be the remedy to fall OUT of love. Because I truly didn't think about HIM the whole time I was doing my EX!!!

I'm going back to the online dating game – If I'm attracted to you, I will do you and move to the next.

BEST DISTRACTION EVERRR!!!

Day 13: Working The O.C.

SO, I did some more research and decided to join Zoosk. Well, the truth is, it was the online dating website that required the least sign-up expense, and my experience with Match.com hadn't been so great. I could join for thirty days. If I can't find a distraction in thirty days, I just need to give up anyway. I didn't feel like wasting time in the game, so I need to do this right quick. So, whoever contacts me needs to be "REAL" real quick. As my best friend, Pam, says, "We don't have no more time to deal with men who have "potential to have potential!"

Right now, I'm not trying to get married or even get Boo'd up, I'm just trying to forget HIM and move on. Of course, someone cute and with the desire AND ability to treat me to some finer things in life would be nice.

Almost right away, I start getting e-mails from men on Zoosk. As I'm looking through their profiles, I'm like – "No, No, No, and NO!!" Are you on crack?? NO!!!

Wait, back up...here's one that looks interesting...

Nice smile, handsome, six feet tall, no kids at home, fifty-five...He could work. He lives a little far from my liking,

Huntington Beach, but I could let him buy me a meal or two…or three. A sista NEVER turns down a free meal.

His message is short and sweet – "Hi Phyllis (I'll explain that later), my name is Danny, I like your smile and your humor. I would love to meet you. E-mail me if you would like to connect." Hmmmm, I don't know…I hadn't planned to REALLY go out with anyone else this soon. I just wanted to maybe message or e-mail someone for a while, and then talk on the phone for a while. I didn't actually want to personally meet so quickly.

DAMN!! What am I??? Twelve years old? So, I e-mail Danny back. "Hi, Danny, my name is really Kayla. Phyllis is just my screen name. I would love to perhaps meet you for coffee. I'm in Chino Hills. Let me know when you're in the area."

I figured I'd give him a few days to see if he responds. I'm nervous as hell. I'm not trying to be Catfished!! We know what happened the last time I tried this on Match.com. This is probably some 400 pound, ugly ass fourteen-year-old girl pretending to be this cute beach man hottie. I ain't playing with these people. I'm not gonna be all nice and polite like these people on t.v.

I'm looking for a RealMan.com.

But I can't think about it too long. Of course, it's one of those chaotic Real Estate days. Wait, let's keep it real, ALL Real Estate days these days are chaotic. I'm either dealing with sellers who are losing their homes and don't really want to sell or want to sell the house for much more than it's worth. Or, I'm dealing with buyers who either don't have enough money to buy or who has champagne taste on a beer budget. Sometimes, my clients are perfect, and the parties on the OTHER SIDE OF THE TRANSACTION IS CRAZY!

Anyway, it's my job, and I LOVE it, maybe because I'm crazy and a glutton for punishment??!!

I'm going through my hundreds of e-mails I receive daily

because my partial OCD won't let me do otherwise. B.I.N.-GO.!!! I've got an e-mail from Danny, the guy from Huntington Beach!!

Well, Well, Well,....., what does he have to say??!! He's probably going to say, "Lady, this is why you're single – your profile is ridiculous!!"

But, here goes nothing...I open the e-mail.

"Hi Kayla, I would love to meet you for coffee at your convenience. How about Monday? Your choice of when and where. I know that you live in Chino Hills so we can meet there. I'm excited to meet you. Have a great day."

Okay, well, that was pretty anti-climactic. No, I cannot tell you what I was expecting, but not that.

I'm gonna think on this for the day...

4 Hours Later.....

I'm ready. I think I'm going to do this darn thing. If I don't start dating now, I know I'll start finding all kinds of reasons to get back with "HIM," and that's just NOT an option. So, I booted up the computer, logged into Zoosk, and e-mailed dude back. "Hi Danny, a coffee meet and greet sounds perfect! I have an appointment at 12:00 on Monday, but I can meet you at 11:00 a.m. at Starbucks in The Spectrum South in Chino. It's on the corner of Pipeline and Grand Ave. I'll let you know Sunday what I'll be wearing so you know it's me. I'm looking forward to meeting you. Kayla"

Notice I used the term "meet and greet," I don't want him thinking it's a date. I also slid in that bit about an appointment so I can cut it short if it's a "no go."

I pressed "send" and ....sigghhh...

Let's see....

Day 14: Down With The Swirl

THERE ARE some days that you'd like to re-live over and over again. And then, there are some days you wish had never happened... Those two days are the same in my case − the day I met HIM.

THIS shit was what I woke up to. I mean, who wants to wake up to thoughts like this every freaking morning???!!! Waking up with that on my mind just sets the tone for my entire day. No wonder I've been such a bitch to my co-workers lately. I don't know how they can stand me − I can't hardly stand my own ass right now!!

Something is gonna have to change....and I mean... right...the hell...NOW!!

Meditation....Yeah, meditation. I need to look into that. Oprah and Deepak Chopra have this 21-day program. I can't control the thought that hops into my mind in the morning, but I can sure change lanes and control my thoughts for the rest of the day!!

Well, at least today is a day off, so I don't have to deal with Real Estate madness.

But, of course, the madness from other people don't stop just because I say so....I get a text from HIM:

"Missing your love so much. Why did you need to do me so wrong? I still love you. I have tried everything, and nothing compares to you. I just want to hear your voice once more."

This fool done lost his rabid ass mind!!

It took me a few minutes for my rage to reach full bloom. It finally dawned on me that not only does he feel that he can contact me with this, "I miss you" bullshit whenever he gets lonely **orrrrr** when whatever **THOT** doesn't work out, and he gets horny, but he has the NERVE to say **I** did **HIM** wrong???!!!

I can't even....

I was about to text him back a nuclear bomb, but my common sense popped her head in and said, "Self, NO!! it's not worth it." So, I said, fuck him, and threw my cell phone under the couch.

ASSHOLE!!! He got me fucked ALL the way up.

Feeling like I need to "shake him off" before my little date from the internet tomorrow, I called my friend, Kim. I asked her if she wanted to meet at The Yardhouse for a quick martini and flirt. She said Yes, so I flat ironed my hair and put on one of my cute sundresses and some four-inch wedges. Hmmm, that'll work, nothing like watching men watch you to remind me that I'm his loss. AND, give me a little extra confidence for tomorrow.

The Yardhouse, for some reason, is jam-packed this evening. As soon as we walk in, Kim eyeballed some cuties. I'm kinda down with "The Swirl" right now anyway, and I see several prospects too, but one has seriously caught my eye. About 6'2", 190 pounds, sandy blond, blue eyes, and the most sensuous smile I've seen in a minute. Just as I'm getting a little excited, Kim bursts my bubble. "They're Cops...the whole group." I was like, "Girl, how you know that?" Kim gave me the black girl look – you now, head tilted to the right, lips turned up, left hand on left hip… "Hmmph, trust me….I know."

Damn!

I don't like policemen. I mean, I LIKE policemen as a group, but I don't want to date one. I've had several girlfriends tell me NEVER to date anyone in law enforcement. Apparently, they are controlling and aggressive, exactly what someone like me DOESN'T need.

But, this one is fine as hell, and he keeps staring….can't I just play with him for a minute??

As Kim and I order our drink, four of the guys we spotted make their way over to our side of the bar. Of course, the one I'm eyeballing stands toward the back, and his other two friends step up to "make my acquaintance." One of his friends is black, muscular, and pretty handsome.

Men are so shady, though. THISSS Negro spent the entire time trying to let me know, low key, that his friend wasn't suitable for me. But, I felt the chemistry coming from the back of the group, so I focused on it, and it soon became obvious. Finally, I reached my hand toward him and said: "I'm Kayla." He stepped a little closer and said: "My name is Wesley." Kim about died and said, "that's my son's name." And, then, I point-blank asked him, "are you a Police Officer?" He chuckled a bit and said, "Why do you think that?" I was about to speak, but Kim jumped in, with her blocking ass, and said, "Because I can tell. The haircut, the build of your body, the way you guys carry yourselves." He laughed and said, "Yes, my friend is Orange County Sheriff," then points to the other friend, "Los Angeles County Sheriff, and I'm a Profiler."

"THE FUCK???" This IS NOT gonna be good – I do NOT want to be profiled. I like my skeletons right where the hell they are – IN MY CLOSET!!!!

But bruh is FINE!!! I could feel the electricity between us. We were both looking into each other's eyes and smiling. I asked him,

"So, Mr. Profiler, you can observe me for a while and tell me all about myself?" He started laughing and said, "well, I have a feeling there isn't a great enough Profiler in the world to do that." Now, it's my turn to laugh, because at least the man is honest!

He says, "but, I am pretty good at being able to tell when someone is NOT telling the truth. That's what I do – interview people for the truth."

Interesting….because if I don't do nothing else….it's tell the truth…So, I should be good. I leaned in a little closer to him, seemingly accidentally, sliding my knee between his legs (I'm sitting on a bar stool facing him, and he's still standing up). I look him dead center in those gorgeous blue eyes and whisper, "Have I been telling the truth?"

He's a little flustered, but he's goooood…He leans in even closer to me and says, "I think I'm gonna need a little more time."

Damn!!! Bruh isss good….

We chit and chat for a bit. Finally, Kim and I tell him we're gonna head out. His friends have long gone, but he walks us to my car, gives me a quick appropriate "because I just met you" hug and says, "Since I know where you work, would it be okay to stop by or call you sometime soon?"

I like that!!!

"I'd be disappointed if you didn't," I tell him.

As he's walking away, Kim and I low key high five!! When he's far enough away, I whisper to Kim, "I like him!" That feels good to say because I haven't said that for a long time.

Day 15: Some White Man Shit

WELL, I slept pretty good. I didn't even dream about HIM. I mean, I'm not gonna lie – a wet dream isn't the worst thing to have, but if I keep thinking and obsessing about those moments of our time together, I promise you, I would never get him out of my system. Because, REALLY, there was no better, more passionate time in my life than my time with him. The reality is that I've accepted that I'll never have anything like that again. His body type, his assertiveness, his stamina, his thorough knowledge of a woman's body, his sensuality – all of that.... plus my intense love for him......I won't find that package again. So, I can't risk continued dreams and thoughts about that.

OH, LORD!!!

Just then, I went somewhere....WOOO SAWW, bring it back, Kayla!!!

But, see, meeting someone like Wesley could be just what I need. Just Fine as Hell because...Just strong, don't need me, just kinda want me...And, I'm certainly ready for the swirl (google that too) again.

Wesley kind of hinted that he would come by my office, and I'm looking forward to it and need to be ready. So, evaluating my closet, I picked out my shoes first. Shoes kind of set the tone for the whole outfit. Wesley was over six-feet tall, so my four-inch Michael Kors peep toe heels will be perfect. After adding a white professional blouse and a form-fitting black skirt that fell below the knees, it was the perfect "sexy professional" I wanted to portray. Not too much jewelry. My silver hoops with diamond chips (yes, chips...I have a son in college whose mother is the ONLY one writing college checks, so ALL I can do right now IS "chips"). I added some light make up with a shock of pink lips, and I was ready to get to the office and a surprise visit.

The work day is good, but lunchtime comes and goes, and there's still no pop in visit from Wesley. By about four p.m., I realize this punk ain't coming by. I mean, my feelings are hurt. I thought we had serious chemistry, and I just KNEW he was interested in me as well. Maybe he's trying not to look too anxious by coming by the first day after meeting. Are men still playing THAT stupid game??!! I mean, we're grown ass people...REALLY???!!!

Of course, you know what I gotta do now.....I GOTTA CALL ONE OF MY GIRLS...I need another opinion on this. So, I call Kim since she was with me last night.

"Kim, what you doing?" I'm trying to act all nonchalant, but I can't even help it. I go right in before she can even respond with a hello. "Girl, do you know that guy I met last night hasn't even called me yet?" Kim was like, "What??!!, you gave him your phone number, right?"

"Noooo, but I told him where I worked. He's a fricking Police Officer, I figured he'd figure it out and come by my office today. He did say, "maybe I'll swing by your office and say hi." Kim started laughing, "Girl, that was just yesterday. You know men don't like to seem too eager. He'll probably wait a few days."

"Pshhh," I sputtered. "Girl, we are grown ass people in

our fifties. I am NOT playing that high school game. If you snooze, you lose."

BYE, FELICIA!!!

See, just like that, I was over IT and Wesley.

I packed up my briefcase and went on home.

But, I did stop by Vons to pick up a bottle of Pinot Grigio.

Maybe my "date" tomorrow with the guy I met on Zoosk will lift my spirits and keep my hope alive.

Day 16: Stick To The Plan

I WOKE up feeling like a schoolgirl before the first day of high school. You know that, "what do I wear, change clothes four times, hair won't do what I tell it to do, make-up tripping, that. FORGET IT!!! I don't want to do this" feeling. Finally, you get that to "whatever, this is as good as it's gonna get" feeling. He's gonna get what the hell I got to give.

I think I walked out of my door at about 9:00 a.m.

I looked down at my stomach and butt.

DAMN!! Maybe it's time for a butt lift, and a sit-up or two once a week wouldn't kill a sista....

Oh, Well!! Not bad for a fifty-three-year-old mama of four and gramma of four. HIM is gonna miss me something bad.

The morning seemed to drag on and on before my date. I kept looking at my cell phone − to check the time and look at his profile picture.

But then, why was it fifteen minutes before we were supposed to meet, and I wanted to cancel the whole thing??

But, a quarter till eleven, I pulled my big girl panties up and headed on over to Starbucks.

Now, I'm a big believer in "sticking to your plan," so I reminded myself of my plan:

1. Remind him that I have an appointment at 12:00, so can only stay about twenty minutes.
2. Be "professional" nice, not "on a date" nice.
3. Don't give personal info – address, work location, etc.
4. Park a little bit away and make a "Red Carpet" entrance
5. No physical intimacy – hug or kiss. You see, it's not about playing games, because I'm not that girl, but this is internet dating. You don't know their intent and, I'm not trying to be an episode of The ID Network.

I took my time "sashaying" from the parking lot, taking my time.

I spotted and recognized him right away. He didn't realize that I saw him because I had on huge wraparound sunglasses, and he couldn't see my eyes.

Now, let me explain something. I chose this particular Starbucks for a reason. From 11:00 until about 2:00 p.m. – It's always packed, especially with businessmen between the ages of about forty-five to sixty-five. And, whenever I come here during that timeframe, about five heads swivel and watch me walk up when I'm dressed to the Nine's.

So, when I meet this guy, I want him to notice me being noticed. I think it will heighten my desirability to him. See – there is a method to my madness.

Just like I planned, I had on my good dress and four-inch heels, so about four or five heads looked up. I walked right on by my date like I didn't know it was him. As I walked by him, he called out "Kayla??" I stopped, smiled, and turned around. "Danny?" (I had told him what color dress I'd be wearing). His grin was wide, so I could tell he liked what he saw. He leaned in to what I thought was a hug, but we're not breaking rule number five, so I sweetly smiled and put my hand out to shake his. "Hi, nice to finally meet you," and sat down in the nearest chair.

I'm checking him out discreetly behind my sunglasses. He's attractive, probably a little older than he said he was. He said fifty-five, but I think he's maybe sixty, but a good sixty.

He immediately stands up and asks if he can get me something to drink.

HE GETS A POINT for that!! That reduces the point that I was getting ready to take away for telling that AGE lie.

Let me just go ahead, get this out of the way, and be politically incorrect and make my black men mad. For the most part, that's some white man shit! I'm speaking in generalities, but most black men will sit across from you and let you choke with thirst and NOT offer you a drink if they even THINK they have to pay for it. So, if you mad brothers, I'm sorry – do better. I'm just keeping it One Hunnerd. Take a tip – offer a woman a drink. If you can't afford that, you shouldn't even be on the date.

Anyway, we had a pleasant time. I liked him, age lie and all. I kept the conversation light, what do you do, how often are you in this part of town, yada, yada, yada... I was going to save the "how come your last girlfriend dumped you" conversation for the third date. After about thirty minutes of good conversation, I looked at my cell phone and let him know that I was glad that we met, but I had to head out to my appointment. He immediately asked if he could have my phone number, call me later and plan a date for the weekend.

I said yes, gave him my phone number, stood up, and said, "I look forward to hearing from you, bye," and dashed off. I wanted to leave him a little unsure, and I didn't want him to walk me to my car.....AND NO, I DID NOT LOOK BACK AS I WALKED AWAY.

I checked my cell phone about thirty minutes later, and he had texted me. "I really enjoyed meeting you. I like you, and can't wait to see you again. Drive safe."

Now, that's sweet. I think this moving on thing is gonna be fun....

Day 17: Never Saw It Coming...

I DON'T NEED YOU, I don't need you...but I want you."

I woke up with a start, with this song by Jhene Aiko pounding in my head. I had a feeling something was wrong, and I kept hearing a chirping sound. It took me a minute to realize it was my cell phone. I look at the phone and realize that it's fucking seven a.m. I don't get up that early, and EVERYBODY knows that. Who's texting me that early???

GOD, NO!!!!

It's HIM....

Whaaaaat DO YOU WANT???!!!

The text reads, "Tina is going to call you. I need you to quit-claim on the house we have on Cameron so I can sell it."

WTF???!!!

I don't even know what the hell....and then it hits me like a ton of bricks. I totally forgot about that house he and I bought together 5 years ago. He was trying to sell it and wanted me to just quit claim my interest to him??? I was wide awake now, my heart beating so fast that I could barely catch my breath.

THE FUCK???!!

Just then, my phone rang. A 480 area code. It must be

Tina, the Realtor. I let it go to voicemail. I just couldn't do anything except lie there for about ten minutes, but then I couldn't help myself, I checked my voicemail. I wanted to cry, once I realized who it was. It was Tina, and she apologized for calling, but was trying to sell the house for HIM and needed me to sign a quit claim deed so he could close escrow.

I called my "then" best friend, Marilyn. "What should I do??" I'm thinking she was gonna say "Hell NO, make his ass buy you out!" But to my surprise, she said, "Girl, you said you want to move on, to be rid of him, get him out from under your skin. This may just be the way. You'll never be able to forgive him for this one. I say, do it."

All I could say was, "I don't know."

Just then, another text came through. "Good morning, Sweetie. I hope you have a great day." It was from Danny, my Zoosk coffee date from yesterday. Maybe ALL men aren't bad, just the ones I fucks with. Pshhh…let me get up and get ready for work.

But, all day, my mind kept going back to that text. For the REAL first time, I had to wrap my arms around the fact that it may truly be over. He really didn't love me and that I finally needed to move on. And, I'm finally pissed off. Not even at him, but at my damn self. What is wrong with me that this is a surprise??

Am I REALLY one of those women that say, "I never saw it coming?"

I barely made it through the day without breaking down. I got home, but I can't tell you what I did throughout the whole day. Had the one thing that I said I would never let a man do to me been done? Had I let HIM break me down to my knees?

They say that the mind defends itself as long as it can. I believe that. My mind is shutting down and trying to convince me that HIM was an anomaly, that they weren't all fucked up.

The problem is – he wouldn't be the first one. So, how many times could my mind protect me?

I needed to immerse myself elsewhere, so I decided …Yes, it was a decision to become what all men pray they don't meet…A Woman Scorned.

I called Danny from Zoosk.

"Hi, Danny, this is Kayla. I was so glad to hear from you today. I'd love to see you again."

He was excited…and we made a dinner date for Friday night.

At that point, I became a Woman on a Mission. And, you don't want to know what that mission was...

Day 18: The Power Is In The Vagina

IT WAS A TUFF ASS NIGHT. I tossed and turned all night and woke up with an extremely sore back. Although I woke up with a calm soul, and a clear mind, my stomach feels empty and restless. I didn't understand why I felt that way because I've met a really nice guy who seems to be totally into me.

I'd like to think that the only reason I was thinking about HIM all night was because of this damn property title issue. But, oddly enough, I'm okay with that. Marilyn is right. I need to do the right thing and sign the quit claim deed and let him sell the property if I'm trying to move on. I don't want the property, and to do anything else would just be spiteful and ugly... And, you know how I feel about doing ugly. I guess it was my last piece of hope that someday...

I cannot get over the fact that his bitch ass couldn't at least call me himself and ask me to sign it. I can't even believe that I wasted over eight years of my life in love with his silly ass! I feel like he just threw gasoline all over me and then stood back and watched me burn. I know that's dramatic, but it's true.

I figured I'd better get on up out of bed and try to reach back to how I felt last night before I fell asleep. A Woman On A Mission....But what exactly is my mission? To take a chance, risk something? It just dawned on me – I'm not meant to be perfect, I'm just meant to be whole. And relying on any man to make me whole was the biggest and longest running mistake I've been making my entire life.

Someone (a woman, no doubt) once said: "Women hold the key to a mans happiness, the power is in the Pussy." It sounds a bit crass, I will admit. But it's true. Think about it, we have what they ultimately want, so why aren't we smarter with it? A lot of us are out here giving it away Willy Nilly, just handing it out for a $1.89 Tuesday Special at Popeyes. It doesn't mean we use it to get over on a man. It just means that we need to know our strength. I am beautiful, I am smart, I am kind, I am fun, I am funny, I am sexy, AND I have a vagina….how am I chasing someone who obviously isn't smart enough to know what he could have???!!

THAT part of me on a mission?? She made twenty calls, made five appointments, and met yet another guy while grocery shopping at Vons. He walked up to me… "Excuse me, but you look very familiar." Game recognize Game, so I said, "I'm sure I'm not THAT familiar," with my head cocked to the right side and a little smile on my face. He shows me The Homes Magazine, which is a Real Estate Advertising Magazine, in his hand. That is me on the cover. I chuckle and say, "I suppose I might be a LITTLE familiar." He says "Well, I have to be honest…I don't want to sell my house, but I'd LOVE to take you to dinner sometime?" I say, "Well, I'm in the magazine because I want to sell homes, but I suppose I have to eat sometimes."

WHAAAAT??? I'm single!! I think I should be dating at least three men at a time until I meet "That Guy."

Ladies, you know what I mean. The Guy that money can't buy. So, I'm making a plan, and I'm sticking to it. I know, I know – I've said it before, but this time I'm executing the plan. Until I figure out what I truly want in a man, I will not give even a fraction of my heart away. Now, let's be realistic –

every woman desires companionship and affection. So, I'm not saying I'll stop meeting men or stop dating. Hell, I LOVE dating. I LOVE the feeling of a man desiring and adoring me.

Oh – What's my plan, you ask??? To date...often and many. I'm going to date as many men as I can meet that meets my basic criteria.

What is that, you say? Here's where I sound vain and selfish...and I...don't...care...

1. Good Looking – a "seven" and above
2. Financially Fit – he doesn't have to be rich, but he needs to be comfortable and not struggling
3. Funny – gotta make me laugh and he's gotta laugh...and not that ugly sarcastic humor. I hate that kind of humor.
4. Fun – just every time we're together we have fun... even if we're just watching Golden Girls
5. Lives Alone – No roommates and no children living at home
6. A Gentleman – he opens doors and offers help without being asked to
7. Thoughtful – he can anticipate my needs and desires
8. Romantic – yeah
9. Passionate – at least four times a week...yeah, it's like that
10. And I need three...That's right – T.H.R.E.E.

I'm not trying to get married, or Boo'd up for at least two years. I've got some work to do on myself first, and I want a little variety until I decide to get serious. So, this new guy I met online might just be Dude #1.

Let's see.

Day 19: Comfort, But No Fireworks

TODAY IS my first dinner date with Dude #1. I don't know why, but I'm a little...no, a LOT...nervous. I haven't been on a first date in literally eight years! This shit is crazy. I'm excited about possibly having male companionship again. Someone to laugh with, hold hands, and watch movies with. Okay, have sex with. I'm just saying.

But, honestly, I just don't know if I'm ready to move on. Moving on means opening myself up to most likely the same shit ...again. Because at the end of the day, women are crazy as hell, and men are just clueless. And, unless the stars are lined up and the moon is in the right place when you meet a man, it's gonna be work. Sometimes an extreme amount of work, maybe a lot of work, or maybe just a little work. But, work, nonetheless. It's hard. I was talking to Pam, and we came to the conclusion that our expectations of men may just be too high. We're expecting perfection from them, and they could NEVER meet that bar. We also admitted that we may be a LITTLE high maintenance and a wee bit crazier than just that normal "Woman Crazy."

So, is it possible to have exactly what we desire?

Maybe not, but we decided that we bring a lot to the table,

so it's perfectly acceptable that we demand a lot from a man. It just means that the pool of men is much smaller for us. Smaller…can I live with that? Well, I'm just going to have to stay single because I refuse to settle. I mean, I'll work with a man that obviously has the ability and desire to be what I want, but I won't live every day regretting my choice – THAT'S WHAT'S NOT GONNA HAPPEN!!!

It was a busy day at work. I love most of the aspects of my job. For a single woman, it's a good opportunity to meet men. The problem is, most of the attractive and powerful ones (the ones that turn me on) are already married. I guess at my age, they should be. I'm kind of suspect of any man who's single after the age of fifty.

So, what does that say about me, right??? LMAO.

I always ask men why they're still single, pushing for details about why the last relationship failed. Though I know most men will put most of the blame on the woman (she was crazy, she was a Drama Queen, she wouldn't have sex with me, etc.), it's important to me what is said and HOW it's said. I want to detect signs of woman bashing, still in love feelings, bitterness, baby mama drama, but most importantly, the inability to take ANY responsibility for the end of the relationship.

Danny called and asked me where I wanted to have dinner and at what time. In retrospect, that should have been a red flag for reasons that may not be obvious to you yet, but they will later. I chose Wood Ranch in Chino Hills. It was close to my home – which is important for the first date. You should be on your familiar ground. It was also pricey enough to see if this type of date will financially strap him, but not over the top expensive. It was quiet, with a nice upper middle-class aura. It would give us the chance to casually communicate and for him to see how I "GET DOWN."

He was familiar with the restaurant since he actually designed and installed most of the signs in the mall that the restaurant is in. I just told him meet me there since I didn't want him to pick me up at my house. I'm still not ready for him to know where I live.

I decide to dress "Sexy Business" because I'm not sure how he'll be dressed, and it's a nice restaurant. Plus, I'm always sexy. I'm getting dressed, the hair is on point, the makeup is very casual with an emphasis on my MAC "Heroin" lipstick. I'm wearing a white semi see-through flouncy blouse with my black and white demi bra and my leather pleated and flouncy skirt. I added a couple of dots of Dolce & Gabbana "Light Blue" perfume. I throw on my black and white Michael Kors heels, and I'm not gonna lie… I AM SIZZLIN!!!

I'm putting on my final touches and my phone burps. A text. I'm looking at the phone, thinking, "That mofo better NOT be calling to cancel!!"

But, when I pick the phone up, it was a text from HIM:

"Hey, my friend, just checking up on you. Hope all is well. Miss my friend, we once were good friends."

WHAT THE HELL???!!!

What am I supposed to do with that text? GO AWAY!!! What does it even mean? We were NEVER good friends. We were lovers, and then it came to a disastrous end. The fact that we made several attempts at reconciliation and each time HE brought it to a crashing end with his dishonesty, indecisiveness, and pure arrogance insured that not only would we never be friends but that we never were.

I'm not gonna lie, he was there for me during my chemotherapy, but only in the manner that suited him and the entire time he was trying to date two "friends" of mine. I think he actually did, but neither he nor they will ever admit it….But, a woman KNOWS.

A complete and totally arrogant asshole, that's what he is. Good in bed, now, but still an asshole.

I wasn't going to respond to the text at first. But, after re-

reading the text and formulating different responses in my head (most of them too vile to repeat), I finally decided that I needed to respond, that I needed to let him know that I've moved on:

"All is GREAT with me. I hope you're good. TRUE friends always stay friends."

There, mothafucka!!!

Shit!!! Now, I'm gonna need to go to church...and I'm pissed off.

He's trying to just KEEP me on that emotional rollercoaster. I've fooled myself for too long, thinking that some part of him was good for me. I said to myself right then, "Self, HE was NEVER good for you. It was just around and around, up and down. Over and over again."

I'm getting off this roller coaster. I never liked roller coaster rides anyway!!

I've got a date to go on, and a mind to blow.

I know that I'm going to sound pretty conceited now, but after I parked and walked through that parking lot towards Wood Ranch, heads were turning. The Wood Ranch in Chino Hills stays packed, and I got there a few minutes late intentionally. I wanted to let Danny see me walk up, but to also watch him, watch other men watch me walk up.

I think it's important for men to see that other men SEE us so they can appreciate what they have the potential to have. And, after that text from HIM, I have an attitude.

I'm almost at the door of the restaurant, and I see him standing a bit to the left of the door. I was disappointed! Here I am, all dressed up, and he's dressed like he's going to a job. Not even a professional job, a JOBSITE. Now, don't get me wrong, I don't have a problem with men working a blue-collar job or on a job site. As a matter of fact, I'd be in seventh heaven if I met a Sanitation Engineer. Shooooot...a good steady job with a pension. Heyyyy!! But, if you're taking a woman on a first dinner date to a nice restaurant, FOR ALL

THINGS HOLY, dress up a bit!! Don't show up in tennis shoes, old polo shirt, and jeans. I mean, I'm dressed UP!!!

So, needless to say, I've already formed an impression. But, Ima do this. I'm dressed, I'm out, I'm irritated about that text, and I'm hungry. I might even get dessert.

I have to say, the date was surprisingly pleasant, his attire aside. At least he let it be known that he was painfully aware that he had underdressed. He said, "Every time I see you, you're dressed nice and sexy. I guess I underdressed for the evening." And, he said it in a sincere, sweet way, so I decided it wasn't necessary for me to embarrass him more by telling him, " Yes…you are underdressed."

The conversation was light but fun. He's a gentleman, I give him that. He told me that I could order whatever I wanted. Trust me, I watched his facial expression CLOSELY while he was looking at the menu to see if his eyes widened when he noticed the prices. He even moved his chair closer to me when he realized that other men were watching me – I like a LITTLE jealous.

Afterward, we walked around The Shoppes. It was a great evening, with him trying to walk close to me and hold my hand.

It seemed like he didn't want the date to end, and the goodnight kiss was sweet. Not too over the top, a respectful first date kiss. I haven't had a chance to ask for his medical report, so there won't be none of that "swapping spit" just yet, Homie. He tried to linger a bit, but I had to cut it off. I think below his belt was getting a little excited.

I drove home, texted him that I made it home safe, and when he got home, he texted me that he arrived home.

I don't know where this is headed. I have to be honest and admit that I didn't feel fireworks, but I felt comfort. I could take the time to get to know him but….

I don't think he's THAT guy.

Day 20: Black Man Swag

I'M FEELING PRETTY good today. Danny texted me this morning just to say, "Hello." I know that I said he wasn't THAT guy, but I think I could work with him and make him "THAT" guy. Or, maybe I don't need "THAT" guy right now. All I'm really trying to do is kick this habit for HIM. I've been so wrapped up in this other ugly relationship for so long. Why am I even trying to go there, trying to figure out if another man can be THE man so soon? That's the problem with women. We're so busy trying to fill up any gap in our lives that we don't even stop to think that a temporary gap is a good thing.

I mean, I'm intelligent, hardworking, fun, in good shape and fairly cute. I don't know why I'm in such a rush to find another man to replace the last one. Why can't I just take some time and breathe??

You see, this is one of those instances where I start thinking about the differences between Black women as opposed to other women. Other women know how to DATE. They don't think every man they go out with, meet, or even have sex with has to be their "Boyfriend." Black women think if they "go out" with a man, they have to be in a committed relationship. How are we going to get these men out of our system if we don't just date and have a little fun?

It takes time to get to know someone and decide if he's even someone you want to spend any type of quality time with. That can't happen in two dates. Here I am, just went out on the first REAL date with the man, and I'm already trying to decide if he's THAT guy. How about I just take my time, enjoy what the man has to offer and have a good time. Hell, how about I take my time and enjoy what several men have to offer and have a good time??

I said earlier that I thought my expectations of a man might be too high, but I think that the real problem is that the expectations of myself are just too low. It's okay to expect a man to be a man. I don't think I want to settle, I want to have what I want and if it takes me a little time and a few men to find that....well, so be it.

I didn't have any Real Estate appointments the rest of the day, so I decided to just relax, clean my house up a bit, and cook a good meal. I did just that, but early evening I went back on Zoosk on my quest to meet more men and perhaps find a few more that I could date. I don't want a boyfriend, and I'm not trying to find a husband. I just want to have a little fun and totally get HIM out of my system. But, I did feel a little nostalgic. A day like today would be one that HE and I would do just what I was doing, clean up a little, laze around, read books, watch movies and cook. And I'm missing that. That's what I miss the most – the companionship, the familiarity, not having to try hard to conversate. Conversate – is that even a word?? I don't think so.

I flip through Zoosk at the e-mails I've received. There are dozens. It seems like everybody is looking for somebody these days. WOW…

Hmmmmm, I found one intriguing…he SAYS he's sixty (but we know how they lie, right?), but he is handsome. He had nice eyes, but was a little shorter than I was hoping for –

5'8". I may not be able to wear my high heels, but I don't think men trip about that anymore. Look at that little bitty Kevin Hart. He's dating someone about a foot taller than him, and she proudly wears her high heels. Okay, I'm not a model, and I'm not dating a celebrity with his own rules of dating and life, but you get my point. And, I'm surprised, this guy is an ex-police officer and a Congressman. What??!! I'm suspecting that he's a liar. Why would a Congressman be on a dating site? Something must be wrong with him. But, he lives in West Covina, not too far. He's Black, and I am kind of missing that Black man swag. And if he's a liar, it will just cost him a cup of coffee and a Donut. So, I accepted his request and moved on to the next. The next one I see is a cute white guy. He says he's some Executive that lives in Brea. Okay, close, so I accepted his request too. What the Hell…right? I had nothing to lose but a couple of hours, and I might just meet my Soulmate. It's happened to other people.

Day 21: Chasing The High

I WOKE UP CRAVING HIM. I don't know, maybe I had a dream that I couldn't remember, maybe it's still this property title issue, or maybe it's the fact that everyone around me seems to be in a loving relationship. I know things aren't always what they appear to be. Maybe the people that seem to be in these happy relationships aren't really all that happy. But for whatever reason, the day started out hard.

Oh, wait, I know!!! It's because it's DAY 21, the day I was supposed to be over this thing. I tell you the devil is a liar!! I thought that it was only supposed to take twenty-one days to kick a habit. It's been twenty-one days. In a lot of ways, I still feel like I felt twenty-one days ago.

Funny, though, my thoughts on HIM now only revolve around the sexual relationship. Together, we were like fireworks. But, my cravings for him stop there. The only time the other parts of our relationship that were good was the first two years. I guess that's what kept me wanting HIM, the memories of that time. Our times together were romantic and fun. Even when we were doing nothing but watching Sex and the City together (yes! He did that for me), we just chilled and cuddled. He even watched Queer As Folk and Will & Grace with me while giving me a foot rub! So, I miss the sweetness that was HIM.

I remember getting a massage once, and as the masseur was massaging my arms, I had a severe flashback to HIM. Sometimes at night, he would give me THE BEST massage AFTER bathing me! Yes, he literally bathed me sometimes.

So, as I sit and think, I realize now what's held my addiction to him so strong and long. It's because I missed who HIM used to be and was still living with the hope that the original HIM will return. I read more about how addicts stay hooked on Heroin and Meth. It's kind of like after the first high, and then they chase that high again. They can never find it, but keep going back to the drugs in search of what they felt the first time.

Well, I see now the original feeling, the original love... it's not the same, and it never will be.

Here's the thing - I could go after HIM and get HIM. But, HIM is NOT good. It never was. It was an illusion, and everyone that knew him warned me. HIM, just like drugs, would fool me, trap me, and try to destroy me - just like the devil. HIM means me no good at all, and I finally see that.

Sure, I know there will be times that I stumble in my journey to stay away from HIM, and GOD forbid if I actually indulge in a little bit of HIM. But, I'm finally crystal clear that HIM is not what I want. I want a life free of HIM, a life without such complete and deliberate destruction to my soul. It's dangerous.

Today is the day - twenty-one - and I'm supposed to be able to break away from him, to pull him outta my system.

But, what I've realized is that love is NOT like smoking, exercising , dieting, or being on drugs. After someone has gotten under your skin and in your heart, there is no way you can un-love them in twenty-one days or even twenty-one months.

I admit it…My name is Kayla, and I'm still in love with Lee…

But, I'm safe because, as Taylor Swift says, "WE ARE NEVER EVER EVER GETTING BACK TOGETHER AGAIN!!"

I won't go back into the dark. I do still love him…Perhaps a bit less, but I still do…But, I don't want him back.

I also realize that I don't need to be in a serious relationship for a while. I'm good with me because the pickings are definitely slim. I could write an entire book on mine and my friends' dating exploits!!

What have I learned? I've learned that you can't get over one man or fall out of love by replacing them with another man. When you're deeply in love with someone, there's a part of you that will always be in love with them. It becomes intertwined with your blood…your DNA. When you hear a certain song, watch a certain video, or go to a certain place, it all rushes back. That feeling can crush you to your very core because you didn't properly grieve the loss of an ENTIRE part of you. You may have grieved and mourned the loss of your partner, but that's not the same. You lost an integral part of yourself, and you have to give that time to heal. You need that time, time to re-build your soul and fall in love with "You" again. Otherwise, you settle for someone sub-par. You move from encounter to encounter, never quite getting what you're looking for. In the process, you end up losing an even larger part of yourself.

I'm good. I'm still in love with HIM, but little by little, I am definitely moving on ONE DAY AT A TIME!!

DAY 22: How It Played Out...The End..Or Not?

HOW IT PLAYED OUT...THE END?

TEXT FROM DANNY:
"Hey Kayla, I had a great time and hope you did too. I was wondering if you'd like to come out to Huntington Beach Sunday to hear a Reggae Band. I'd love to spend more time with you. I like you."

TEXT FROM LEE:
"Hey, Baby, I was really missing you today. Realizing that I may have lost my one true love and wondering why you don't love me anymore. What am I to do?"

MY RESPONSE TO DANNY:
"I had a great time too. Thanx so much. You are a Sweetie. Sunday sounds good. I'll call you tonight to confirm and get details."

MY RESPONSE TO LEE:
"What am I supposed to do with that??!!"

THE END

WHAT I'VE LEARNED through these "Rehab" days is that
you attract what you put out there. I was spending so much
time focusing on what I didn't want that I was ensuring that's
exactly what I kept attracting, my connection and desire for
him. What I'm focusing on now is to be happy and satisfied
with life. I'm confident that what will come to me now is fun,
happy, and positive friends, Also Known As "Higher Compan-
ions". I think something is coming and I'm just gonna have to
wait patiently for it.

No, I didn't fall out of love in twenty-one days, but I did
learn how to move on. I suppose you have to take the pain
with the pleasure. The scariest part is letting go because you
then realize that Love is a Ghost of Expectations that you
can't control. And at the end, you have to ask yourself, "Self,
will I disappoint my future if I stay in this relationship?" If the
answer is yes, then you've got to keep stepping and get it
OUTTA YOUR SYSTEM...because these men are a MAZE
OF COMPLEXITIES.

So, what happens next? I'm just going to keep on keeping
on. Drinking Martini's, selling homes, and Swiping Right. If
Danny doesn't work out, the next one just might.

Made in the USA
Columbia, SC
28 May 2020